# *Risk and Promise*

# Risk and Promise

## a handbook for parents adopting
## a child from overseas

Ira J. Chasnoff, MD
Linda D. Schwartz, PhD
Cheryl L. Pratt, PhD
Gwendolyn J. Neuberger, MD

Chicago

For a complete product catalogue write to:

NTI Upstream
180 North Michigan Avenue
Suite 710
Chicago, Illinois 60601

Or

Visit our website at www.ntiupstream.com

*Risk and Promise: A Handbook for Parents Adopting a Child from Overseas*. IJ Chasnoff, LD Schwartz, CL Pratt, GJ Neuberger.

Library of Congress Control Number: 2006929165

ISBN-10: 0-9707762-5-X
ISBN-13: 978-0-9707762-5-9

# Contents

## Part II   Understanding your child's risk and protective factors

### Part III  Work Sheets for observing your child overseas

# Introduction

Children adopted from overseas often have had a rough start in life. Whether living in an orphanage or a foster home, whether from China, Russia, South America, or Vietnam, these children bring unique challenges to their adoptive families. While the risks that their backgrounds pose often capture the most attention, it is important to also consider the strengths that these children can bring into their new home. The source of this resiliency may be extra attention received from a particular caregiver in the orphanage or foster care setting, or it may be the child's inherent personality or his innate intelligence. Whatever the case, it is essential to remember that an adopted child, just like every other member of the family, brings strengths and weaknesses, joys and challenges, successes and frustrations into the family. Ultimately, it is the love that the child brings and receives which defines the new family that is created with each adoption.

Every adoption is the culmination of a long series of challenging decisions, but parents contemplating adopting children from overseas have a unique set of considerations. *Risk and Promise* is a handbook designed to help prospective adoptive parents navigate the often puzzling array of information and decisions attendant to the process of international adoption. The purpose of this handbook is to help you better understand the risk factors as well as the protective factors an adoptive child from overseas can present, support you through the decision-making process, and guide you during the period of transition in your lives as your new child moves into your family.

Of course, the "success" of any adoptive placement is a function of not only the capabilities and needs of the child, but also the expectations, characteristics, and lifestyle of the adoptive family members. It is important that prospective adoptive families assess their tolerance for uncertainty, for the potential challenges that the child may bring, and the parents' ability (financial and otherwise) to modify their lifestyle in order to accommodate the demands of a child who may be quite challenging. Along these lines, a secondary objective of this handbook is to enlighten prospective adoptive parents regarding the extent of what may be required of them if, indeed, they are to fulfill the commitment that they are making in taking on the responsibility for a child whose needs will unfold over time.

*Risk and Promise* cannot make the decision of whether you should adopt a particular child. Ultimately, only you can make that decision. What this handbook can do is offer you the advantage of the authors' extensive research and clinical experience in working with children adopted from overseas. The information you gather will support you in making the best decision possible for your family. While there are no guarantees when considering adding to a family, the more informed you are, the better able you will be to guide yourselves and your family toward a positive adoptive experience.

When you first begin to use *Risk and Promise* we suggest that you familiarize yourself with the book's general information so that you can be well-informed as you enter the process. When you are presented with a child available for adoption, you can return to *Risk and Promise* and look up specific characteristics and read about the risk and protective factors as they relate to your child.

The first two sections of *Risk and Promise* provide you with information as it will come to you during the adoption process. Each major section is then divided into key subsections that focus the information on specific characteristics related to your child. The book's third section consists of worksheets that you can fill out to help you collect baseline information that will be helpful in both the short and long term.

If you have concerns or questions after completing *Risk and Promise*, it is advisable that you contact a professional who has experience in working with children who are adopted from overseas. But be careful! The fields of medicine and therapy for children adopted internationally are specialized, so be sure to find professionals who understand the needs of this unique population of children. Classically trained pediatricians and therapists, although expert in their particular disciplines, often lack familiarity with the specific needs of children adopted from overseas.

Once you return home with your child, early intervention is essential to facilitate your child's developmental progress. And it does not stop at early intervention. Many of the children will face life-long challenges, and the parents must be sensitive to the needs of their maturing children as they enter progressively demanding environments and encounter growing societal expectations. While some children do make remarkable progress once they are in a nurturing environment that provides appropriate stimulation and opportunities for learning, many children will need additional intervention in order to remediate delays. The neurological, prenatal and environmental risk factors that may contribute to their difficulties often warrant assistance from the Early Intervention System, Early Childhood Special Education programs, school programs, and private specialists and therapists. Given the risk factors faced by internationally adopted children, it is important that intervention be sought whenever there are concerns, prior to the emergence of more serious problems with emotions, behavior or development.

Early intervention programs also can serve as a support system for parents, helping them to adjust to and accept the reality that their child is following a developmental trajectory that may or may not resemble that of "typical" children. Without this support, it is easy for parents to be overwhelmed and as a result feel inadequate or, worse, letting their disappointment and frustration affect the relationship with their new child.

Parents must train themselves to be attuned to their children and to the degree to which the children may be exhibiting inappropriate behaviors. Bring these behaviors to the attention of professionals with whom the children interact. Many times professionals, especially within the school system, do not feel comfortable initiating discussions regarding perceived problems; they tend to gloss over concerns for fear of alienating the parents, and as a result, if the parent does not take the lead in establishing open and honest communication, the problems become more severe later on.

Adoption is a long-term commitment, and it is important to have all of your questions and concerns addressed as completely as possible as you move forward with opening your family to a child. If you have concerns, please visit our web site at www.childstudy.org, through which you can request a consultation with one of the authors of this handbook.

# Part I Pregnancy and the newborn

## Chapter 1
## Maternal history and newborn status

When prospective adoptive parents receive medical and other background data on a child born overseas, there usually is very little solid information to go on. In fact, parents and physicians often find themselves reading between the lines to try to glean some insight into the risk factors that may affect the child's long term prospects. However, much can be learned by understanding the impact of what may seem to be minor bits of information about the birth mother and her pregnancy.

A note of caution, though – no international adoption agency can guarantee the accuracy or completeness of medical or developmental information contained in the child's reports. In addition, many families face being asked to accept a referral on the spot in-country, without having the benefit of a medical professional assessing the child prior to making the commitment. In all circumstances, gather as much information as you can, utilize any resources available, but in the end, trust your gut instincts. And never be pushed or rushed into a decision until you are completely comfortable.

## *Life in the womb*

Before we start our review of what the various aspects of maternal and birth information mean, it is important to understand that teratology – that is, the study of birth defects – is an inexact science. This is the part of the child's life – from the mother's genetic and family background through the time the baby is born – about which you will have very little, if any, information.

The developing fetus is susceptible to many of the complications that occur among women overseas who make their babies available for adoption. Poor nutrition, infections during pregnancy, and the use of unregulated medications are the most common problems, but there are many other factors that place the baby at risk. Some of these are factors about which the prospective adoptive parents do not have information, but others are data that can be gathered and used to assess the potential level of risk faced by a particular child. For example, the age of the birth mother often is included in the medical records parents receive. But such information about the father is rare, even though the age of the father at the time of conception can be important in fetal development. Even the age of the maternal *grandfather* at the time of birth of the baby's mother has been documented to be a significant factor in the child's acquiring the bleeding disorder Hemophilia A.

Confusing? You bet! And the lack of any kind of reliable family history in overseas adoptions just makes matters worse. Add to that the fact that little is known about what really happens when normal development in the womb is disrupted and why this leads to such varied problems in the baby, and you can appreciate why making long term predictions about the baby's outcome is so difficult.

But even with the many complications and unknowns, there is information that can be of help. Our best advice is to use the information you have as much as you can, and don't worry about what is not possible to uncover. The following sections provide insight into the most common information you will come across during the pre-adoption process.

## Maternal age

Girls who become pregnant during adolescence bring with them a host of difficulties, because adolescents who become pregnant often have engaged in multiple high risk behaviors in addition to unprotected intercourse. This is true whether the teen aged girl is living in the United States or overseas. Pregnant adolescents have a higher rate of illicit drug use and alcohol use, especially binge drinking, than pregnant women in their 20's and older. In addition, pregnant adolescents are less likely to get adequate prenatal care, are more likely to have poor nutrition, and are more likely to have sexually transmitted diseases. Foreign adolescents who become pregnant also are more likely to have the additional risk factor of living in dire poverty.

At the other extreme, babies born to women over 35 years of age, especially if it is the mother's first pregnancy, are more likely to have chromosomal defects, most notably Down Syndrome. In the United States, most pregnant women over the age of 35 years will have an amniocentesis and chromosomal testing of the fetus. However, such testing will not be available for pregnant women giving birth overseas who offer their children for adoption. Although many chromosomal abnormalities are diagnosable at birth and usually will have been recognized prior to the baby's being placed for adoption, prospective parents may wish to have the added certainty of genetic testing once the baby arrives in the United States if they know that the birth mother is over the age of 35.

## Maternal nutrition

Many women from overseas whose babies are available for adoption live in poverty and thus have little access to a fully nutritious diet. The earliest recognition of what vitamin deficiencies can do occurred in 1933, when it was found that a lack of Vitamin A during pregnancy can cause malformations of the baby's eyes, mouth, and kidneys. Another study then showed that a lack of riboflavin during pregnancy resulted in changes in the baby's skeleton structure. There are several other examples of vitamin and mineral deficiencies producing problems in the child, including a lack of folic acid intake during pregnancy producing spina bifida (incomplete closure of the spine) in the child.

Generalized malnutrition is just about a given among the mothers of babies available for adoption. Problems associated with this more general form of malnutrition were documented during World War II. Using time before the war and after the war as controls, scientists studied the effect of a 3 to 4 month food blockade of Holland imposed by the Nazis, during which the urban population of the country had a markedly decreased intake of calories and vitamins. They found that 50% of the women stopped having periods, and nine months later there was one-third the usual number of births. For pregnancies already underway, if the mother had been deprived of food during the last three months of gestation, there was a very high rate of babies being born below normal birth weight. On a more positive note, general malnutrition does not seem to interfere with normal organ development in the fetus, and specific malformations have not been identified. Thus, from a practical perspective, the main factor for prospective adoptive parents to look at in relationship to maternal nutrition is the birth weight of the infant.

## Maternal diabetes

Medical records from overseas will sometimes mention that the birth mother had diabetes, a relatively common disease related to sugar metabolism in the body. The association of maternal diabetes with problems of fetal development has been well documented, but the magnitude of the risk to the fetus is controversial. The incidence of birth defects among diabetic women is reported to be from 0 to 20%. The difficulty lies in the various criteria for recognizing diabetes and, especially in overseas pregnancies, determining the severity of the disease in an individual woman.

In one study that reviewed the outcomes of over 7,000 infants of diabetic mothers, 340, or about 5%, were malformed (as opposed to the incidence of malformation of 2% in the general population). Other studies have found three times the rate of congenital malformations in infants of diabetic mothers over the rate of malformation of the controls, and a death rate six times increased. The frequency and severity of the malformations were higher in infants of mothers with more severe heart and blood vessel complications related to their diabetes. When considering only women who are not diagnosed with diabetes but simply have borderline problems of handling sugar in their diet during pregnancy (usually listed as "gestational diabetes" in the child's medical records), there is no increase in infant death or malformation rates over normal pregnancies.

If a baby's mother is reported in the overseas records to have had diabetes during the pregnancy, the prospective adoptive parents should specifically inquire about any evidence of kidney or heart problems in the baby. In addition, the adoptive parents should be aware that a family history of diabetes – including the birth mother's diabetes during pregnancy – places the child at increased risk for developing diabetes himself.

## Number of pregnancies (gravidity)

Women who have had multiple pregnancies (more than 4 or so) and are placing their baby for international adoption often have several associated risk factors, including poverty, poor or no prenatal care, and poor nutrition during pregnancy. However, if the baby's examination at birth is normal, multiple pregnancies need not be considered as an increased risk for the baby.

## Prenatal care

Women who do not seek prenatal care are more likely to have used alcohol or illegal drugs during pregnancy and can have undiagnosed medical problems that can result in risk to their babies. For example, high blood pressure or diabetes during pregnancy can cause low birth weight or prematurity as well as birth defects. However, the problems associated with lack of prenatal care usually can be recognized soon after birth, and the physician can give prospective adoptive parents a reasonable assessment of risk based on this information.

## Duration of pregnancy (Gestational age)

Gestational age refers to the number of weeks the mother was pregnant with the baby before delivery. Babies born from 37 to 42 weeks are considered full term. Parents may find that medical records from overseas will report prematurity in grades of I, II, or III. There is no real consistency as to how these terms are used, however, and it is better if the parents can find out how many weeks gestation the baby was.

Babies born prior to 37 weeks are considered premature, and if they are born prior to 32 weeks gestation they are considered severely premature. Premature birth robs the fetus of the opportunity to reach full growth potential in the womb and places children at increased risk for medical, developmental, and learning problems over their lifetime. In addition, severe prematurity elevates the risk further; these infants often have breathing problems, apnea (the tendency to stop breathing), and increased risk of bleeding into the brain resulting in significant neurological problems, including cerebral palsy. Most of the issues affecting these babies are documented in the first few weeks after birth, and the physicians working with the baby often can give prospective adoptive parents a fairly complete assessment of the child's status.

## Family history

The genetic makeup of the child is a strong factor in determining many aspects of how the child will develop, but equally important is the loving stable environment in which the child is nurtured and raised. Heredity is a significant risk factor for mental illness, addiction, and alcoholism. Adoptive parents should be aware of any family history related to these problems and should be alert for early signs or symptoms.

A family history of alcoholism places adopted children at high risk. Not only do they have a heightened genetic susceptibility for alcoholism in later life, the children of substance abusers frequently exhibit impulsive and oppositional behaviors during childhood and adolescence. As an adopted child approaches preadolescence, her impulsive behavior can place her at great risk for experimentation with drugs and alcohol. Thus, it is important that parents explain to the child her biologic inclination for addiction and the need to avoid experimentation, a usual challenge of adolescence.

# Chapter 2
# Newborn growth

The size of a newborn is a key indicator of her overall health status while in the womb. Growth charts have been developed by the United States Centers for Disease Control and Prevention that allow for the comparison of a newborn's growth to that of other babies at birth. Copies of these growth charts can be found in Section III of this handbook. The growth parameters of interest are the newborn's weight, length, and head circumference.

By using a growth chart one can determine if a baby's growth falls in the normal range. For example, if the baby's weight plots out at the 25th percentile, this means that he weighs more than 25% of other male newborns his age. Strictly speaking, weight, length, and head circumference that plot out between 3rd and 97th percentile are considered normal. However, it should be noted that some clinicians view the 10th to 90th percentiles as the normal range, and some states use a definition of 5th to 95th percentile for being defined as "normal" growth.

One of the caveats of this assessment of growth is that the growth charts that are available are based on the growth patterns of children born and raised in the United States. Unfortunately, comparable reliable growth charts for children born overseas have not been developed. When we evaluate the growth of children adopted from overseas we must thus consider their size in the context of their country's standards of growth.

Another important point is that children who are premature are going to be small. The following information is based on measurements for children born at full term (38 to 42 weeks). If a baby is premature, then the measurements have to be adjusted for gestation age based on duration of the pregnancy. In general, the rule of correction is adjust for prematurity until the child is three years of age when measuring length, until the child is two years old when measuring weight, and until 18 months for plotting head circumference.

## Birth weight

The average birth weight of full term babies in the United States is 7 pounds 8 ounces, with a normal range down to approximately 5 pounds

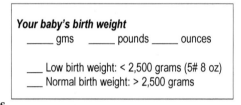

**Your baby's birth weight**

_____ gms   _____ pounds _____ ounces

___ Low birth weight: < 2,500 grams (5# 8 oz)
___ Normal birth weight: > 2,500 grams

8 ounces. Any baby weighing less than 5 pounds 8 ounces is considered to be a "low birth weight" baby. When reviewing medical records, you sometimes will see that a child has "intrauterine growth retardation." For practical purposes of this discussion, this term means essentially the same as low birth weight.

Low birth weight is a reflection of poor growth in the womb and is a significant problem in many babies born overseas. Tobacco smoking or the use of alcohol or other drugs of abuse can significantly affect the fetus' growth, as can poor nutrition or generally poor health during pregnancy. Although as the child grows, he usually "catches up" to a normal weight for age, low birth weight is a significant risk factor for developmental outcome as the child gets older.

Medical documents from Russia and other former Soviet bloc nations frequently refer to low birth weight I, II, or III. In general, this refers to mild, moderate, or severe growth impairment, but there are no established guidelines that define these levels.

## Birth length

The average birth length of term babies in the United States is about 20 inches (52 cm), with a normal range down to about 18 inches. In general, reduced length alone is not a significant marker of risk. However, if the baby is very short at birth, this might be an indication of some type of genetic disorder which would require further investigation.

### Birth head circumference

Head circumference (the size of the head) at birth is very important because it is a reflection of brain growth in the womb. The average head

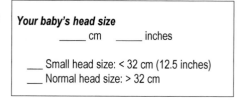

**Your baby's head size**

_____ cm _____ inches

___ Small head size: < 32 cm (12.5 inches)
___ Normal head size: > 32 cm

circumference at birth for a full term baby is about 35 cm (13 inches). A head circumference below about 32 cm (12.5 inches) at birth is small and is an indication of risk.

The growth of the baby's head is stimulated by the growth of the brain. Therefore, babies born with small heads often have had poor brain growth in the womb. Alcohol, cocaine, and heroin are among the substances of abuse that have been shown to be most closely associated with poor brain growth. Genetic abnormalities and infections in the womb (toxoplasmosis, rubella, syphilis, cytomegalovirus, herpes) are other causes of small head size in a newborn. In addition, it has been noted that many infants born overseas who are placed in orphanage, especially in Russia and other eastern European countries, have a small head circumference, although the reason for this has not been determined.

A small head circumference at birth is a significant marker of risk for poor developmental outcome. Studies of newborns with small heads have shown that the head size does not usually catch up to the normal range, and if it does, it can occur as late as when the child is four to five years old. In some cases, especially if the mother drank alcohol during pregnancy, the head size continues to be small throughout early childhood and into adulthood.

## *Symmetric and asymmetric growth retardation*

The general long term outlook for a child born too small can be assessed by comparing relative birth weight to head size. A small head size at birth accompanied by a low birth weight (symmetric growth retardation) reflects overall poor growth in the womb and represents a greater risk than that of children with only low birth weight. In cases where birth weight is normal but the head is small or both weight and head size are low but the head circumference is proportionally more reduced than the birth weight (asymmetrical growth retardation) the risk to the child is even greater. This often is the case in babies adopted from overseas and requires a full neurodevelopmental evaluation to assess the child's status and to put together an appropriate early intervention plan.

# Chapter 3
# Infections in pregnancy
# and the newborn

There is a very high rate of infectious diseases that occur among women whose babies are available for adoption from overseas. The use of drugs and alcohol during pregnancy, high rates of prostitution, and poverty make it more likely that these women will have an infection that can be passed to the fetus.

There are five major infections that must be considered in evaluating the infant available for adoption from overseas: AIDS/HIV, syphilis, Hepatitis B, Hepatitis C, and tuberculosis.

## *Human Immunodeficiency Virus / AIDS*

Acquired Immunodeficiency Syndrome (AIDS) is a disease caused by infection with the Human Immunodeficiency Virus (HIV). It is more prevalent in substance abusers and prostitutes than in any other populations. HIV is passed through sharing needles as well as through sexual contact. It would be best if every pregnant woman whose baby was going to be placed for adoption were tested for exposure to HIV. If the woman was tested early in pregnancy and the test was negative, a repeat test should be performed in the third trimester of the pregnancy. If the test is negative in the third trimester, it is unlikely the child has been exposed to the AIDS virus. However, regardless of the mother's test results, all children adopted from overseas should have an HIV test at birth or as soon after birth as possible and a repeat HIV test when they arrive in the United States. Although rare, there are a few reports of children who had a negative HIV test reported from overseas, but were positive on follow up testing in the United States.

In the United States, if a pregnant HIV positive woman receives treatment during pregnancy with AZT, the child's chances of having an infection that can progress to AIDS drops from about 30% to 5%. However, AZT therapy is not available in most instances overseas, so this is not a practical consideration.

It is important to know that regardless of the mother's treatment, any baby born to a woman who is positive for the HIV antibody will also have a positive test. However, the positive test in the newborn may be due to the transfer of the mother's antibody across the placenta rather than to a true infection in the baby. In order to determine whether the infant really has the AIDS virus it is necessary to perform a more sophisticated test such as a PCR test or an HIV culture on the baby. These tests are available through most major medical centers in the United States and can differentiate the babies who are truly infected from those who simply temporarily carry their mother's antibodies but who will not go on to develop an infection or AIDS.

Prospective international adoptive parents sometimes are told that a baby was HIV positive at birth but currently is negative. It generally takes 12 to 18 months for a baby's HIV test to turn negative. No matter what the age of the baby, it would be best to have PCR testing performed to confirm that the child is negative; however, such testing is rarely available in overseas adoptions. Therefore, in a case where an adoptable child has a history of a positive HIV test, prospective parents must carefully weigh the risks before making a decision about adoption.

## Syphilis

Syphilis is a sexually transmitted disease that can cause severe structural and neurological complications in the infected infant. If syphilis in a baby goes untreated, the child will have significant medical complications that affect the teeth, the brain, the bones, and most other organ systems. State laws in the United States require that all pregnant women be tested for syphilis, and most hospitals test all women at delivery if previous testing is not documented. Overseas, pregnant women are usually tested for syphilis during prenatal care or at delivery. Therefore, in most instances, it is easy for adoptive parents to learn whether a woman had syphilis during pregnancy.

A diagnosis of syphilis is dependent on identifying the organism in the blood (a spirochete named *Treponema pallidum*) or detecting antibodies that a person develops to fight against the organism. The most commonly used tests for syphilis both in the United States and overseas are Venereal Disease Research Laboratory (VDRL) slide test and the rapid plasma reagin (RPR) test. If the birth mother's test for syphilis is negative, or if it was positive and she received adequate treatment with penicillin, the baby is unlikely be affected. However, an untreated case of syphilis during pregnancy can cause severe complications in the newborn.

Congenital syphilis is contracted from an infected mother's placenta during pregnancy. If untreated, 40% of these pregnancies result in spontaneous abortion. Affected infants may have a variety of serious symptoms soon after birth, including large liver and spleen; nasal snuffles; enlarged lymph nodes; lesions of the mucous membranes of the mouth, throat and eyes; changes in bone structure; rash; anemia caused by breakdown of red blood cells; and/or a deficiency of platelets in the blood which causes a tendency to bleed. Untreated infants may develop late manifestations, including problems with their central nervous system (brain), bones and joints, teeth, eyes, and skin.

Most children born overseas who are available for adoption were tested for syphilis at the time of birth or at the time of placement in foster care or an orphanage. Any child born to a mother who has a positive test for syphilis or whose mother had a positive test for syphilis but did not receive adequate treatment should be treated with a complete course of penicillin. This will protect the child and prevent long-term complications. Syphilis is particularly common in the former Soviet Union and physicians there tend to over-treat newborns for syphilis; although it may not be necessary, this does not cause harm to the baby. While discrepancies are not common, it is recommended that children adopted from overseas be retested upon arrival in the United States.

## Hepatitis B

There are several forms of Hepatitis, a viral disease primarily affecting the liver. The two forms of greatest concern in pregnant women and their babies are Hepatitis B and Hepatitis C. Hepatitis B and Hepatitis C can be transmitted sexually as well as through shared needles in drug users and therefore occur more commonly in the drug-using population and in women who have had multiple sexual partners.

If a pregnant or newly delivered woman has a negative Hepatitis B test the newborn should receive the first of a series of three vaccines against Hepatitis B before leaving the newborn nursery. If the mother's Hepatitis B test is positive, an additional medication is given to protect the infant. These therapies protect the baby against becoming infected with Hepatitis B, even if the mother is infected.

When managed appropriately, Hepatitis B is not usually a problem for parents adopting domestically. However, Hepatitis B testing of pregnant women overseas is less consistent and therefore careful documentation of testing and results are necessary.

In overseas adoptions, if the mother's Hepatitis B test is documented as negative, then the child should have a negative test and have received vaccines against Hepatitis B. Whether or not the vaccine was initiated prior to adoption, the adoptive parents should be sure to follow up with the full series to ensure optimum protection.

If a child does come down with Hepatitis B acquired during intrauterine life, the child can suffer significant liver damage and, ultimately, liver failure. There is no specific treatment for Hepatitis B, and it has lifelong implications.


## Hepatitis C

Although HIV infection rates are plummeting in the United States, Hepatitis C rates are burgeoning in the drug and alcohol using populations, and a resultant increased rate of infection is being seen in children available for adoption. This is especially true in all the countries that are allowing international adoptions. Fortunately, more and more of these countries are conducting Hepatitis C testing so that prospective parents will have some basic information.

There is no treatment for Hepatitis C, and no one is quite sure what the clinical pattern is for children who have been affected in the womb. However, we do know that Hepatitis C can take up to 25 years to cause any problems. In the United States, Hepatitis C is one of the most common reasons that people need a liver transplant. Parents as they adopt need to know if the child has been infected, and thankfully, more and more nations are testing babies available for adoption for Hepatitis C infection; however, it is hit and miss, and there are many countries that do not have the capabilities to test.

If a pregnant woman has Hepatitis C infection, the likelihood of transmission of Hepatitis C from mother to infant is about 5%. The rate of transmission is higher if the mother is also HIV positive. Testing and evaluation of newborns and children for Hepatitis C is very complex. The following outline is a summary of the approach to testing for Hepatitis C:

1.  If the initial *antibody* test performed in the baby overseas is negative, it is highly unlikely that the baby has Hepatitis C. However, the test should be repeated once the baby arrives home. If the test in the U.S. is negative, no follow-up antibody screen is needed unless the baby is less than six months old. In this case, a repeat test at six months is warranted.

2.  If the initial antibody test is positive, it is still unlikely that the baby is infected with Hepatitis C due to the relatively low transmission rate (5%) from mother to baby. However, a PCR test must be done in order to clarify whether the baby is actually infected with the virus or simply temporarily carries the mother's antibodies but will not go on to develop an infection with the Hepatitis C virus. A PCR test for Hepatitis C done at 6 to 8 weeks of age has about a 20% chance of being a false negative. (A false negative is a blood test that is negative, but the baby actually is infected.) The reliability of the test to confirm the absence of the disease gradually increases with the age of the child, so that by 6 months of age, the chance of a false negative test is about 10%. Because of this, many experts recommend that a PCR not even be done until 6 months of

age. However this is not helpful for families trying to gather information to make a decision about adoption. In such a circumstance, it is reasonable to perform a PCR test at 6 to 8 weeks of age. If it is positive, the family can use that information to guide the decision with the awareness that the test is not 100% accurate. If the PCR test is negative, the family can make their decision knowing that there is an 80% chance that the child does not have an infection with Hepatitis C according to the test. Since the overall likelihood of transmission of Hepatitis C from mother to infant is about 5%, statistically the baby *probably* is not infected.

3. When analyzing information about Hepatitis C, it is also important to know the child's HIV status, because transmission of Hepatitis C is significantly higher in cases of simultaneous HIV infection.

## Tuberculosis

Children born overseas make up more than one-third of newly diagnosed cases of tuberculosis in the United States. Indeed, this often is the motivation behind hospitals' establishing "International Adoption Clinics" in the first place. Children can be infected during pregnancy, after delivery by exposure to the mother, or can catch tuberculosis from another person in the orphanage or foster home. While most tuberculosis infections are symptom-free, those individuals who do present with problems usually do so approximately 1 to 6 months after infection. Symptoms include a cough that will not go away, fatigue, weight loss, loss of appetite, fever, coughing up blood and night sweats. Infants and young children will most likely present with failure to gain weight and developmental delays.

The cornerstone of tuberculosis testing relies on the Tuberculin Skin Test or Mantoux test. With this test, a small amount of inactivated tuberculosis protein is placed under the skin to determine if the body develops a rapid response to the protein. Someone who has been exposed to tuberculosis develops an area of red swelling around the testing site. Swelling of greater than 10 mm is considered a "positive" test. While the test appears to be quite straight-forward, in practice there is a great deal of variability between evaluators and how they measure the reaction on the skin.

Most babies adopted from overseas have received the vaccine against tuberculosis, the BCG. It appears as a scarred dimple on the child's upper arm. The BCG vaccine complicates matters when evaluating the child, because if a person has received the BCG vaccine prior to the skin test, he will test weakly positive even though he may not have been exposed to the actual tuberculosis bacteria.

Despite having received the BCG, all children adopted from overseas should have a tuberculosis skin test immediately upon arrival in the United States. If the child has a positive skin test she should have a chest X-Ray done. If the X-Ray is negative, the child should be placed on an oral medication – Isoniazid (INH) – for nine months. If a child is found to have active TB, complete with symptoms and a chest x-ray suggestive of acute infection, treatment becomes more complicated, and the child should be followed closely by a tuberculosis specialist.

### Summary interpretation of test results

The table provides a summary of the interpretation of test results for the five major diseases of concern along with the appropriate follow through. It should be emphasized that no matter what the test results overseas demonstrate (positive or negative) all tests should be repeated upon arrival in the U.S. If a child's tests for any of the infections are negative overseas, no further testing should be performed until the child comes home. Then all tests on the child should be repeated.

## Test Results and Infant Follow up for Some Infectious Diseases of Concern in Pregnancy

| Disease | Mother's test | Infant's test | Infant follow up |
|---|---|---|---|
| AIDS | HIV negative | HIV negative | none, although should be repeated test when child arrives home in the U.S. |
| | HIV positive | HIV positive | PCR (25% chance of infection in baby) |
| Syphilis | RPR negative | RPR negative | none, repeat test in U.S. |
| | RPR negative | RPR positive | treatment with penicillin, repeat test in U.S. |
| | RPR positive | RPR positive | treatment with penicillin, repeat test in U.S. |
| Hepatitis B | HB negative | HB negative | Hepatitis B vaccine, repeat test in U.S. |
| | HB positive | HB positive | Hepatitis B immunoglobulin Hepatits B vaccine, repeat test in U.S. |
| Hepatitis C | HC negative | HC negative | none, repeat test in U.S. |
| | HC positive | HC positive | PCR blood test (5% chance of infection) |
| Tuberculosis | usually unknown | PPD negative | none, repeat test in U.S. |
| | | PPD positive | chest X-Ray, treat with INH oral medication, further therapy if CXR + |

# Chapter 4
# Maternal alcohol and
# drug use

Frequently in international adoptions, there is no information available about a woman's use of alcohol, tobacco, or illicit drugs during pregnancy. However, some studies have estimated that at least 13% - 45% of the children from the former Soviet bloc nations and Romania have Fetal Alcohol Syndrome and another 60% were exposed prenatally to alcohol. These numbers are much lower for children from other countries, although there does appear to be growing risk of heroin (opium) use by women from the Asian countries and Central and South America. In addition, cocaine, heroin, and marijuana use in the South American countries continues at high levels, including among women of child bearing age.

Urine toxicologies are not done on pregnant women delivering babies overseas, and many of the acute problems in the newborn related to alcohol or drug use by the mother will not be recognized nor mentioned in the medical records available for review. However, it is important that prospective adoptive parents understand the early and long term implications of prenatal alcohol, tobacco, and other drug exposure. In the following sections, we will discuss the basic impact of each of the substances on the newborn and infant and then provide some information regarding long term implications for your child.

## *Alcohol*
Fetal Alcohol Syndrome (FAS) is the original name given to a cluster of physical and mental defects present from birth as the direct result of a woman's drinking alcoholic beverages while

she is pregnant. Individuals with Fetal Alcohol Syndrome have findings in three categories:

1) Growth deficiencies

2) Central Nervous System involvement

3) Facial Dysmorphology

The mother's confirmed use of alcohol is not necessary to make a diagnosis of FAS if the child meets criteria in all three categories; however, physicians should note when the diagnosis is made without confirmation of the mother's drinking.

Unfortunately, there is quite a bit of misinformation concerning prenatal alcohol exposure and FAS. Alcohol exposure at any point in gestation can cause significant problems for the child, although exposure in the first trimester is the only time that facial features are affected. Thus, even though a baby may "look normal," there can be significant impact.

## Growth deficiencies

In the United States, the average birth weight of babies born at full term (38 to 42 weeks gestation) is 7 pounds 8 ounces, with a normal range down to 5 pounds 8 ounces. Babies born to mothers who use alcohol have an average birth weight of around 6 pounds and are more likely to weigh less than 5 pounds 8 ounces. As children with FAS grow older, they tend to continue to be small for their age – that is, short and underweight. Children diagnosed with FAS have either reduced weight *or* height (at or below 10th percentile on standard growth charts) at birth *or* at any one point in time after birth.

## Central nervous system involvement

Problems in the central nervous system can manifest as structural, neurological, or functional/intellectual changes.

### Structural

Children with FAS often have small heads due to poor brain growth. A head circumference at or below the 10th percentile at birth or at any time after birth is a frequent finding in these children. This can be a predictor of poor intellectual function and increased risk of ADHD as the child gets older.

Prenatal alcohol exposure not only causes a child to have a small brain overall but can also stunt the growth of individual parts of the brain. This can occur even in children without characteristic facial features of FAS. Problems with the growth and formation of different parts of the brain can result in a wide range of behavioral and learning deficits. These children can have trouble moving information between different brain regions; they cannot keep information in mind in order to self-direct their behavior or think in the abstract. They may have trouble recording information in the brain and then have difficulty retrieving information they already learned. For example, the child who learns his multiplication tables one day cannot remember them the next. Or, a child has difficulty generalizing information from one situation to a new situation: the child knows not to run into the street that is in front of his house, but cannot apply that information to the street on the side of the house and so runs out in front of a car.

Other parts of the brain also can be affected, resulting in the impairment of the child's ability to coordinate planned motor movements causing impulsive movement and clumsiness. A reduction in the size of the back part of the brain (the cerebellum) produces difficulties with balance and arousal, and may be a source of sleep/wake problems. Again, it is important to remember that such problems occur not only in children with the facial features associated with prenatal alcohol exposure, but also in alcohol-exposed children who "look normal."

*Neurological*
Neurological damage in a child with FAS can be manifest as seizures, strabismus (wandering eye), coordination problems, difficulty with motor control, and a number of less well-defined deficits.

*Functional/Intellectual*
While FAS is as the most common diagnosable cause of mental retardation, not all children with FAS are intellectually impaired. While some children and adolescents with FAS have IQ's that range from as low as the 20's to as high as 135, the majority of the children have IQ's between 85 and 95, which is the low average to average range. Even in the absence of a

diagnosis of FAS, children who were exposed prenatally to alcohol consistently demonstrate lower IQ scores than non-exposed children, and even those with a "normal IQ" demonstrate difficulty with behavioral regulation, impulsivity, social deficits, and poor judgment, causing difficulties in day to day management in the classroom and home.

In fact, a wide range of other functional difficulties are even more common than mental retardation in children with FAS. These include learning disabilities, poor school performance, poor executive functioning (organization of tasks, understanding cause and effect, following several steps of directions), clumsiness, poor balance, and problems with writing or drawing, among others. Behaviorally, many children who were exposed prenatally to alcohol have short attention spans, are impulsive, and exhibit hyperactivity.

For parents, one of the major long-term challenges exists with the school system. Most alcohol-affected children do not meet the criteria for the designation of needing special education, particularly in the early years. Therefore, the child's problems go unaddressed, only to become that much more complicated in late elementary school as the demands become more stringent. By then, damage has occurred not only in relationship to intellectual development, but also in terms of emotional functioning (lack of self-esteem, a feeling of hopelessness, and resulting acting out).

It is important to remember that the impact of prenatal alcohol exposure is not determined solely by the amount of alcohol the pregnant woman consumes. Many reports demonstrate that binge drinking, with high peak blood alcohol levels, is more dangerous than chronic drinking, and long-term studies have shown that even small doses of alcohol are damaging. A recent report involving adolescents noted that as little as one drink per week during pregnancy has a significant detrimental impact on the child's weight at fourteen years of age. Animal studies have indicated that even small amounts of alcohol affect neurodevelopment.

### Changes in facial features

Prenatal exposure to alcohol causes an overall flattening of the middle portion of the face. As a result, children with FAS exhibit:

* epicanthal folds (extra skin folds coming down around the inner angle of the eye)
* short palpebral fissures (small eye openings)
* a flattened elongated philtrum (flattening of the groove running from the bottom of the nose to the top of the lip),
* thin upper lip
* small mouth with high arched palate (roof of the mouth)
* small teeth with poor enamel coating
* low set ears.

## Facies in Fetal Alcohol Syndrome

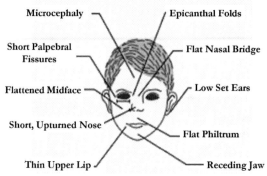

Microcephaly

Epicanthal Folds

Short Palpebral Fissures

Flat Nasal Bridge

Flattened Midface

Low Set Ears

Short, Upturned Nose

Flat Philtrum

Thin Upper Lip

Receding Jaw

These changes can vary in severity, but usually persist over the life of the child. Most people will not recognize any differences when they see the child, but someone with experience working with children prenatally exposed to alcohol will be able to detect the changes. The pictures on the following page are of a little girl with Fetal Alcohol Syndrome. It is easy to see that the facial features do not go away over time, and, although she is quite attractive, her behavior and learning difficulties are significant.

9 months

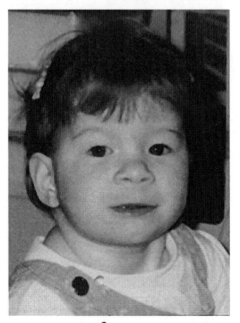

3 years

10 years

11 years

In addition to facial changes, prenatal alcohol exposure can cause a variety of malformations of major organs, especially the heart, kidneys, eyes, and ears. Many children with FAS have vision problems including strabismus (lazy eye). Children with FAS also are predisposed to ear infections and have a high rate of hearing loss (eighth nerve deafness), so a thorough hearing exam is essential. Because the midline structures are poorly developed, the ears often do not drain through the Eustachian tubes well, which accounts for many of the children needing tubes in their eardrums to avoid repeated ear infections.

All this information can be quite confusing for prospective adoptive parents, especially since the language used to describe prenatal alcohol exposure is changing. For the past thirty years, a child whose mother drank alcohol during pregnancy but who had only partial or no physical features of alcohol exposure was said to have Fetal Alcohol Effects (FAE). Although the physical features were absent or minimal, these children had problems in intellectual, behavioral, or emotional development with significant impact on learning and long-term development.

Over the past few years, research has demonstrated that although children with FAE have little to no external physical changes resulting from their prenatal exposure to alcohol, they do have significant structural and functional changes in the brain. This has spurred the development of new terminology. Currently, children who have been exposed to alcohol but do not meet criteria in all three diagnostic categories are described as having Alcohol-Related Neurodevelopmental Disorder (ARND) or Alcohol-Related Birth Defects (ARBD). In April 2004, a group of federal agencies defined a new term, *Fetal Alcohol Spectrum Disorders* (FASD) as:

> "an umbrella term describing the range of effects that can occur in an individual whose mother drank during pregnancy. These effects may include physical, mental, behavioral, and/or learning disabilities with possible lifelong implications."
>
> *Bertrand et al, 2004*

Currently the diagnostic terms that are most commonly used are FAS or ARND, both of which fall within the larger continuum of FASD. FASD is not meant to serve as a specific diagnosis, but rather a unifying term to help clarify the many ways in which prenatal alcohol exposure can affect an individual.

Parents adopting from overseas usually have no specific information about a birth mother's alcohol use. In domestic adoptions, if a woman denies alcohol use and no contradictory records exist, it must be assumed that she did not consume alcohol while pregnant. However, in overseas adoptions, especially for babies from eastern Europe and former Soviet bloc nations, almost the opposite is true – assume that there is a significant risk of the baby's having been exposed to alcohol in the womb.

## Tobacco

Tobacco is one of the most harmful substances a woman can use during pregnancy. It produces a very high rate of low birth weight, prematurity, and health problems in the newborn and child. The rate of Sudden Infant Death Syndrome (crib death) is increased in infants whose mothers smoked tobacco during pregnancy or who are exposed to cigarette smoke in the home after birth. In addition, a woman who admits to using tobacco during pregnancy is more likely to have also used alcohol or illegal drugs. For families adopting from overseas, there rarely is any information regarding tobacco use during pregnancy. In general, the most significant damage from tobacco exposure will occur in the first six months or so after birth, but it is important to realize that children who were exposed to tobacco in the womb have a higher rate of Attention Deficit Hyperactivity Disorder (ADHD) as they reach school age and beyond.

## Cocaine

Cocaine affects the way neurotransmitters such as *serotonin*, *dopamine*, and *norepinephrine* are stored in the brain. Cocaine produces a "high" by increasing the availability of these neurotransmitters at the nerve endings and increasing the excitability of the nerves. The excess neurotransmitter can interfere with blood flow from the mother to the fetus, resulting in poor growth in the womb, and can cause contractions of the uterus, producing premature labor.

Chronic exposure to cocaine can result in the "down regulation" of the neurotransmitter receptors, meaning that there is a decreased number of receptors left at the nerve endings. Positron Emission Test (PET) scans of adults with a long history of cocaine use have shown an absence of functioning *dopamine receptors* in the prefrontal cerebral cortex. The prefrontal cortex is the area of the brain that controls impulsive and aggressive behavior. Animal studies have shown that prenatal exposure to cocaine alters the brain metabolism of neurotransmitters in the motor, limbic, and sensory systems, which results in difficulties regulating different types of responses. All of this information suggests that prenatal exposure to cocaine has long-term effects on the function of the central nervous system in general and on behavioral regulation specifically.

Children who have been prenatally exposed to cocaine may suffer a range of additional physical problems, often based on the interruption of adequate blood flow to developing organs. Cocaine use during pregnancy can result in limb reduction deformities in which the baby is born missing an arm, leg or fingers. There are reports of babies prenatally exposed to cocaine missing a kidney or portions of the bowel due to infarction (death of the organ from lack of adequate blood supply and oxygen).

Brain defects have also been reported in babies whose mothers used cocaine during pregnancy. Small areas of infarction, or strokes, in the brain can occur throughout fetal development or the baby can have a large stroke if the mother takes cocaine toward the end of pregnancy. Similarly, constriction of blood flow to the heart can cause the baby to have a heart attack while still in the womb; heart attacks also have been reported *after* birth in infants whose mothers use cocaine.

Muscle tone – the tension present in a person's muscles – can be very tight in infants exposed to cocaine. This often makes the baby tremulous and shaky and is associated with behavior in which the infant arches his back when over stimulated, draws up his arms and legs tightly, clenches his fists, and curls his toes. Muscle tone changes can also cause the infant to have difficulty with feeding because the cocaine exposed infant chews on the nipple rather than being able to coordinate the usual suck and swallow activity.

Adding to these difficulties, prenatal exposure to cocaine may interfere with the infant's neurobehavior: the ability to interact with her environment, to respond to sound and visual stimulation, and to interact appropriately with her parents or other caretaker. While physical difficulties occur in only about 25% to 30% of infants exposed prenatally to cocaine, neurobehavioral difficulties are far more common and are the basis of many of the more difficult challenges a parent may have in caring for the child.

In summary, the cocaine-exposed newborn with neurobehavioral difficulties can easily become overloaded and has difficulty regulating behavior. Sleep is easily disrupted by sudden changes in light or sound and the infant demonstrates frequent startle reactions and color changes as she becomes over-stimulated. The rapidity of the changes in state of responsiveness can confuse the parent and disrupt interactions between the infant and the parent. It is important to remember that the behaviors the infant is demonstrating are not a rejection of the parent but rather biologically based.

## Marijuana

Marijuana does not have a direct health effect on pregnancy or the fetus; there is no increased rate of preterm labor, growth retardation, or other such complications. However, a woman who uses marijuana is more likely to have used other substances including alcohol, tobacco, and other illegal drugs. More importantly, even though marijuana does not affect pregnancy outcome, it does have an impact on fetal brain development. Long term studies document that children whose mothers have used marijuana during pregnancy have a higher rate of learning and behavioral problems, especially related to plan and follow through with a task.

## Heroin, opium, and other opiates

Heroin, opium, and other opiates are used by pregnant women around the world. They are all narcotics which result in the physical addiction of both the mother and the fetus. The newborn infant is born addicted and goes through withdrawal (abstinence) after birth. Most often in overseas medical charts, the withdrawal is completely ignored, and it would be unusual to find an infant described as having gone through withdrawal. However, parents should be on the look out for cues of an addicted infant who is exhibiting signs and symptoms similar to adults going through heroin withdrawal. The most significant features of the neonatal abstinence syndrome are a high pitched cry, sweating, tremulousness, scratching of the skin, vomiting, and diarrhea (see following table).

### Signs of Newborn Withdrawal from Opiates

| | |
|---|---|
| Neurological signs | Hypertonia (stiff muscles) Tremors Hyper-reflexia (excessive reflexes) Irritability and restlessness High-pitched cry Sleep disturbances Seizures |
| Autonomic system dysfunction | Yawning Nasal stuffiness Sweating Sneezing Low-grade fever Skin mottling |
| Gastrointestinal abnormalities | Diarrhea Vomiting Poor feeding Regurgitation Swallowing problems Failure to thrive |
| Respiratory signs | Tachypnea (fast breathing) Increased apnea (tendency to stop beathing) |
| Miscellaneous | Scratching of the skin Neurobehavioral problems (extra sensitivity to sound, touch, and sights) |

Symptoms of neonatal withdrawal from opiates may be present at birth but they usually do not appear until three to four days of life. However, withdrawal depends on many factors, and in some cases symptoms may not appear until ten to fourteen days after birth. The withdrawal symptoms peak around 6 weeks of age and can persist for four to six months or longer. The infants can also demonstrate many of the same problems as cocaine-exposed infants described above, including low birth weight, prematurity, muscle tone changes, and infant behavioral problems. The reader should review the information in the section on cocaine-exposed infants.

When discussing opiate use during pregnancy, it is important to at least mention methadone treatment for narcotic addiction. Although it would be extremely unusual to find a woman from outside the United States on methadone maintenance during pregnancy, it can occur, and prospective parents should be ready. Methadone is a synthetic narcotic that is used to treat people, including pregnant women, who are addicted to heroin, opium, or other narcotics. The advantage of methadone treatment is that it usually requires only one oral dose each day to suppress the desire to use heroin. The risk of infection with the Human Immunodeficiency Virus (HIV) that causes AIDS or with forms of Hepatitis is reduced when the pregnant woman is on methadone rather than continuing to use heroin or other narcotics. However, it is important to be aware that infants whose mothers are on methadone during pregnancy can undergo the same difficulties as infants whose mothers continue to use heroin through the pregnancy.

## What's next?
In the last several years, research on the effects of prenatal alcohol and other drug exposure has begun to focus on the longer term implications of prenatal substance exposure. Drawing firm conclusions from many of these studies is difficult due to the challenge of distinguishing the purely biological effects of the prenatal exposure from the ongoing environmental problems caused by living in a home with a substance-abusing parent. But these studies still provide us with valuable insight into the potential issues to be faced in the older child who was prenatally exposed to drugs or alcohol.

Studies consistently report that prenatal exposure to cocaine and other drugs, with the exception of alcohol, has minimal direct influence on intellectual development in children once they reach three years of age. It is becoming increasingly clear that the single most important predictor of cognitive development, other than genetics, is the environment in which the child is raised. This reiterates the principle of infant mental health: all aspects of a child's development occur within the context of a positive, secure parent-child relationship.

One study of biologic and domestically adopted children prenatally exposed to cocaine, alcohol and other drugs found that by six years of age, 60% of the children's birth mothers were continuing to use drugs and alcohol. Those children living in homes where there was ongoing substance abuse were also more likely to be exposed to violence: to have been exposed to domestic violence, to have a mother who had been sexually abused or raped, or to have a mother who had previously physically abused a child. Given these issues, it is not surprising that the most important factor predicting the child's IQ at six years of age was the mother's ongoing drug use patterns. A home in which drugs were used was a home in which the child's needs for intellectual stimulation and developmental support were not met.

On the other hand, while prenatal drug exposure may not have a direct effect on

### Behavioral Patters in Children Prenatally Exposed to Alcohol and Illicit Drugs

**anxiety or depression:**
- feels the need to be perfect
- feels unloved
- feels that others are out to get them
- feels worthless or inferior
- feels nervous, anxious, tense
- feels sad and unhappy
- worries excessively

**social problems:**
- acts younger than her age
- is clingy
- doesn't get along with others
- gets teased a lot
- is not well liked by other children

**thought problems:**
- can't get his mind off of certain thoughts
- repeats particular acts over and over
- stares
- has strange ideas

**attention problems:**
- can't concentrate for long
- can't sit still and is restless
- daydreams more than usual
- has impulsive behavior
- has difficulty staying on task

**delinquent behavior:**
- exhibits little or no guilt after misbehaving
- lies, cheats or steals

**aggressive behavior:**
- argues a lot
- demands attention
- destroys his own things or those of others
- is disobedient and stubborn
- has sudden changes in mood
- talks too much and is unusually loud
- has temper tantrums

**poor executive functioning:**
- gets lost in conversations with others
- cannot follow sequence instructions
- difficulties making decisions

the child's intellectual performance, studies do suggest that children exposed to cocaine, heroin, marijuana, and other illicit drugs are more likely to have behavioral, emotional, and learning problems in preschool and elementary school. A typical behavioral pattern that emerges often appears to be Attention Deficit Hyperactivity Disorder (ADHD). What is important is to understand that the behaviors these children demonstrate are based in part on damage to the child's neurological system rather than necessarily being due to willful disobedience.

The accompanying chart provides an overview of the most common problems seen in children who have been prenatally exposed to alcohol or illegal drugs. However, prospective parents must realize that no one substance of abuse can be associated with any one particular problem, and that studies of long term effects are still going on. It also is important to recognize that early deprivation and neglect can produce some of these same behaviors in children long term.

From this discussion it can be seen that it is not easy for adoptive parents to understand and address the complex issues that their children may bring into their new home. These also are the issues that make medication management so difficult in this population of children. The most important point to be made in this regard is that any child before being placed on medication to manage behavioral or emotional problems should undergo a thorough and complete evaluation. It is far too simple to treat the symptoms that we see rather than going deeper to understand what is driving the child's difficulties. There is a reason for every behavior we see, and once we understand the reasons behind the behavior, we can more appropriately develop a treatment plan.

*Risk and Promise*

# Part II  Understanding your child's risk and protective factors

## Chapter 5
## Age at time of adoption

When parents receive their first set of information about a child available for adoption from overseas, two key questions immediately arise: *Should we adopt a younger or an older baby? Does it matter how long the child has been in an orphanage or foster care?* There is no simple answer to either of these questions, especially since there is so little research available to guide our considerations. However, based on the most current information available, there are some general guidelines that can help parents in making a decision.

Common sense tells us that the younger a child is at the time of the adoption, the better the outcome, and available research supports this. Children who have spent less time in orphanages have a better general developmental outlook than those who have spent a longer time living in institutional care. One study indicated that children who spend greater than 23 months in institutional care suffer the most profound impact on brain growth and development. It also is important to realize that there are especially sensitive or critical periods of development that are crucial to long term outcome; many of those crucial periods occur in the first year of life.

Another recent study suggested that children who spend more time in orphanages have lower IQ's and more behavioral and learning problems after three years of age. In children who spent at least eight months in an orphanage, overall average IQ was 90. In children who spent two years or more within institutional care, average IQ was 69. (Average score on a standardized IQ test is 100.) However, any length of time in which a child does not experience individualized caretaking designed to address his needs can have an impact on his cognitive, language, emotional, social and behavioral development. So it appears that there are distinct advantages to adopt a child at as young an age as possible. However, there is a trade off: while younger children who have been adopted earlier statistically have a better prognosis for long-term development, it is admittedly harder to discern specific characteristics and challenges at earlier ages.

On a more positive note, children often can appear to "catch up" in their development when given the appropriate support. At Children's Research Triangle, our experience with children under three years of age has been that most of the children make significant gains in the first six to twelve months after arrival in the United States. A study conducted by another research team confirmed this point. Although 55% of Romanian adopted children had abnormal behaviors (self-stimulation, poor eye contact, abnormal activity level) at the time of initial evaluation, the figure dropped to 36% one year after arrival. Despite the developmental and cognitive risks posed by a history of institutionalization, children who subsequently receive optimal levels of parenting, support, and intervention often make considerable gains following adoption. This initial surge can be misleading, however, and as the child grows and the environmental demands on the child become more stringent (i.e. as the child enters the school system), deficiencies can start to become more discernable. Just because a child has appeared to "catch up" does not guarantee that she is home free. The child must be constantly monitored and assessed based on age-specific requirements and expectations in order to address challenges in a timely manner.

In general, the younger your child at the time of adoption, the less risk of attachment and adjustment problems. Although there is no clear cut-off for the "best" age for a child to be adopted from overseas, there does appear to be a correlation between age at adoption and the severity of attachment problems later. Studies suggest that children adopted after two years of age tend to have more severe attachment disordered behaviors than children adopted by one year of age.

However, in some countries where the child first has to be placed on a list and made available for in-country adoption, adoption any earlier than 9 months to one year of age simply is not possible. If the child is older than six months at the time of adoption from overseas, you should pay particular attention to promoting healthy emotional development in your child. In such cases it will be especially important to understand the effects of early institutional life on a child and employ strategies that will promote resolution of these risks once your child is with you. It may also be prudent to seek guidance from professionals to address issues of attachment as they arise.

# Chapter 6
# Growth patterns and general medical condition

Children's growth is a key indicator of their overall health status. Growth charts have been developed by the United States government that allow for the comparison of a child's growth to that of other children of the same age and gender. The growth parameters of interest are the child's weight, height, and head circumference.

By using a growth chart one can determine if a child's growth falls in the normal range for age. For example, if an 8 year old boy's weight plots out at the 25th percentile, this means that he weighs more than 25% of other boys his age. Weight, height and head circumference that plot out between 3rd and 97th percentile are considered normal. In addition to looking at current measurements, it is equally important to evaluate the child's growth patterns over time.

To plot out your child's weight percentiles, find the child's age along the bottom axis of the growth charts located in the final section of this handbook. Mark the child's weight at each age point for which you have information. This will give you the percentiles in which your child's weights fall in comparison to other children his age.

If your child was premature, correct for the prematurity by subtracting the number of weeks of prematurity from the child's age when you plot the weight. You can follow these same procedures for calculating your child's length and head circumference percentiles. In general, the rule of correction is adjust for prematurity until the child is three years of age when measuring length, until the child is two years old when measuring weight, and until 18 months for plotting head circumference.

One of the caveats of this comparison is that the growth charts that are available are based on the growth patterns of children born and raised in the United States. Unfortunately, comparable, well validated growth charts for children born overseas have not been developed. When we evaluate the growth of children adopted from overseas we are aware of some of the differences that may be due to international comparisons.

## *Weight*

When you plot out your child's weights on the growth charts in the final section of this handbook, you most likely will find that they fall between the 3$^{rd}$ and 10$^{th}$ percentiles for age. This is the lower range of normal weight and is most typical of children adopted from overseas. There is no specific increased risk associated with being between the 3$^{rd}$ and 10$^{th}$ percentiles for weight, although weights in this range can be indicators of prenatal alcohol or drug exposure.

A child whose weight is below the 3$^{rd}$ percentile is significantly underweight; this may be due to multiple factors. Children may be underweight simply because they have not had access to enough food and therefore have not consumed enough calories. Some children are underweight due to disease such as chronic diarrhea, cystic fibrosis, Fetal Alcohol Syndrome, infections from the womb, or other health problems that stunt growth. However, the most common reason for poor weight gain in a child adopted from overseas is a lack of nurturing. It has been clearly shown that even if he eats enough food, a child must be loved and nurtured in order to absorb the calories he is taking in. Children adopted from overseas who have spent their lives in an orphanage or poor foster care situation often have been emotionally neglected and grow poorly for this reason.

It is not unusual for prospective adoptive parents to discover that although their child's weight was normal at birth, her current weight is below the 3$^{rd}$ percentile. Most commonly, the parents will see that weight has continued to fall further and further below the normal growth curves as the child has grown older in the orphanage or foster home. This most likely is due to a combination of factors: poor nutrition, inadequate caloric intake, and chronic neglect. The good news is that the combination of adequate amounts of high quality food and nurturing from committed parents allows many children adopted from overseas to have "catch up growth" during their first year in their new adoptive home. There is no way to predict how much "catch up growth" a child will experience after she moves to her new home, but in most cases children end up falling into the low-normal range of percentiles as they get older.

## *Length or height*

Short stature (length or height below 3$^{rd}$ percentile) is most common in those children whose weights also are lagging below the normal growth curves. However, reduced length or height alone is not a significant marker of increased risk unless the child has a specific medical problem causing the short stature (for example, dwarfism, Fetal Alcohol Syndrome, hypothyroidism). A consultation with a physician to review your child's materials can help determine if significant medical problems are present.

## *Head circumference*

Head circumference (the size of the head) is very important because it is a reflection of brain growth: the growth of a child's head is stimulated by the growth of his brain. Children whose heads are unusually small have often experienced poor brain growth and in general are at risk for developmental delays and learning disorders. There are a variety of causes for poor brain growth, including infections in the womb, family traits, and genetic syndromes. Among internationally adopted children, however, the most common cause is the lack of early stimulation and nurturing coupled with poor nutrition. Exposure to alcohol, heroin, or cocaine during gestation is another possible cause. In addition, infections in the womb such as toxoplasmosis, syphilis, rubella, cytomegalovirus, and herpes also can cause poor brain growth. There are blood tests that can indicate whether a child was affected by these infections, but it is often difficult to obtain these tests overseas.

Studies of children with small heads have shown that the head size does not usually catch up to the normal range, and if it does, it can take several years. In many cases, especially if the mother drank alcohol during pregnancy or if there was an intrauterine infection, the head size continues to be small throughout early childhood and into adulthood. In a recent study of internationally adopted children 5 to 13 years of age who had been exposed to alcohol in the womb, it was found that children with a small head size (< 3$^{rd}$ percentile) had an average IQ of 81, while children with a head circumference above the 3$^{rd}$ percentile had an average IQ of 97. In other words there was a significant difference in intellectual functioning between the two groups of children based on head size.

## *Symmetric and asymmetric growth impairment*

As discussed in the chapter on newborn growth, one predictor of outcome if a child is growth impaired is whether that impairment is "symmetrical" or "asymmetrical." In general, children with symmetric growth impairment have a better long term outlook than children with asymmetric growth impairment in which the head circumference growth lags behind weight growth.

To calculate symmetric vs. asymmetric growth impairment, plot the child's current weight and head circumference. In cases where weight is normal but the head is small (below 3$^{rd}$ percentile) or both weight and head size are low but the head circumference is proportionally more reduced than the weight (asymmetrical growth impairment) the risk to the child is even greater than if weight and head circumference are equally reduced.

If both current weight and head circumference are below the 3$^{rd}$ percentile, find the age on the chart that the weight would fall on the 50$^{th}$ percentile, then do the same for the head circumference. If you find, for example, that your one-year-old child's weight and head circumference both are at the 50$^{th}$ percentile for an eight month old, this is symmetrical growth retardation. However, if you discover that the weight falls at the 50th percentile for an eight month old but head circumference is at the 50th percentile for a six month old, this is asymmetric growth retardation. This often is the case in babies adopted from overseas and requires a full neurodevelopmental evaluation to assess the child's status and to put together an appropriate early intervention plan.

## General medical condition

Most children adopted from overseas present with medical problems no longer seen in the United States. It is strongly recommended that you select a pediatrician before you travel so that you will have access to medical care as soon as you arrive home with your child. The child should be seen by a pediatrician at the most about two weeks after arrival. The doctor will not only evaluate current growth patterns but screen the child for the most common medical problems we see in children from overseas: rickets (Vitamin D deficiency), anemia (iron deficiency), eczema and allergic skin reactions, parasite infections, lice, to name a few. The following medical checklist is provided to guide you and your pediatrician in an initial work up of the child newly adopted from overseas. By performing these tests, you will have screened the child for the most common problems that the children have upon arrival in the United States. If any of the tests reveal a problem, your pediatrician will be able to provide you information for treatment.

## Medical Recommendations for Evaluation of
## Internationally Adopted Children

| Tests | Explanation |
|---|---|
| Complete blood count | Checks for iron deficiency anemia or other types of anemia, white blood cell problems, low platelet counts (low platelet counts can cause bleeding problems in the child). |
| Lead level | Lead poisoning occurs in children who have been chewing on objects painted with lead paint, dirt, and other non-edible objects. Untreated, lead poisoning can cause neurological problems as well as mental retardation. |
| Thyroid function tests | Hypothyroidism can cause growth failure and, if not treated, result in mental retardation. |
| Liver funcation tests | Evaluates condition of liver and detects inflammation from hepatitis. |
| Hepatitis B virus testing (HBsAg, Anti-HBs and Anti-HBc) | Screen for infection of liver with Hepatitis B. If negative, child should be given series of Hepatitis B vaccine. |
| Hepatitis C virus testing | Screens for infection of liver with Hepatitis C. |
| HIV serology | Screens for infection with the virus that causes AIDS. |
| RPR or VDRL | Screens for infection with syphilis. |
| Tuberculosis skin test | Mantoux test even if child has had BCG vaccine against tuberculosis. |
| Stool for ova and parasites | Usually requires treatment if positive, can cause "faiure to thrive," weight loss. |
| Urinanalysis and urine culture | Tests for kidney problems as well as urinary tract infection. |
| Hearing and vision screen | Detects problems that may be too subtle to otherwise recognize. |

# Chapter 7
# Child Development

The decision to adopt a child is a life-changing event, and we know that prospective adoptive parents make this choice with the utmost thought and care. This and the following chapters of the handbook are designed to help you understand your child's potential future developmental needs, so that you can be better prepared to parent your child and help her reach her optimal level of personal growth and development.

While there is developmental risk for all children adopted from overseas, it is important to note that many children experience rapid developmental progress once they enter their new adoptive home. In fact, many parents see significant developmental change as they visit with their child over the first few days after meeting him. Children flourish under the light of loving, individual attention!

## *Information processing*

Before we begin a discussion of child development, it might be helpful to examine some of the basic facts related to how the brain of children (and adults) functions. How we humans handle information is best understood from the perspective of *information processing*:

- Input – recording information (bringing it into the brain),
- Integration – organizing and bringing different forms of information,
- Memory – storing the information in memory for later use, and
- Output – using the information to guide actions, behavior, emotions, language and movement.

Input of information occurs via multiple different pathways, depending on what kind of information it is. Auditory (hearing) information enters the ear and travels along a nerve that inserts in the midline of the brain. Visual (sight) information enters the eye and connects into the back part of the brain. Taste, touch, and smell enter through the top area of the brain. The job of the brain is to bring all this information together – integrate the information – to make sense of it. The information is then stored in the brain as memory and perceptions, and, when it is time, the information is transmitted to the front of the brain (the pre-frontal cortex). The pre-frontal cortex is where dopamine is located. Dopamine is the regulatory center of the brain, responsible for telling the person how to respond to the information that just came in to the brain. In this way, dopamine regulates behavior, emotions, speech and language and most other responses to information.

Optimal development is dependent on the fully functioning brain. Exposure to drugs and alcohol during pregnancy, trauma early in childhood, neglect and deprivation suffered in an orphanage or a poorly responsive foster home – as well as a host of other factors – can affect any point along the pathway of information processing. This is why children adopted from overseas are so vulnerable and at such high risk when it comes to overall or specific areas of development.

### *Cognitive development*
Cognitive development refers to the way an individual perceives, thinks, and gains an understanding of his or her world. Cognitive development is determined by the interaction between genetic and environmental factors. Cognitive development encompasses skills such as problem solving, memory, the ability to learn, visual alertness, creativity, and eye-hand coordination.

Optimal cognitive development occurs within the context of an interactive parent-child relationship in which a child is encouraged to explore his environment, experiment with cause-and-effect thinking, play creatively, and experience novel stimulation. Brain development occurs as the child interacts with the environment in these ways. Prolonged deprivation and lack of one-to-one attention decreases the child's opportunity to stimulate the creation of neural connections in the brain, thereby inhibiting brain growth and development.

Children who have lived in an orphanage or a neglectful foster care environment and who are adopted after age three years are particularly at risk for not acquiring the early cognitive skills needed for later academic achievement. Multiple risk factors contribute to poor cognitive outcomes, including poor nutrition, compromised health status, transient and multiple caregivers, neglect, and prenatal substance exposure. However, there is a broad spectrum of the degree of cognitive delays found in children adopted from overseas, influenced by the country of origin and age of the child, among other factors. For example, one study found that 32% of children adopted from China had delayed cognitive development, while another study found that 16% of international adoptees from 22 different countries had cognitive delays. Whatever the overall rate may be, children who appear to be experiencing delays in cognitive development benefit from early intervention assessment and developmental therapy services, either through the federal early intervention programs for children birth to three years of age or through the schools' special education services for children three years of age and older.

## Speech/Language development

Speech and language delays are very common among internationally adopted children. Over half of children adopted from orphanages experience some degree of language delays. One of the most important factors in language development is exposure to meaningful speech during the first three years of life. Many of the children's speech and language delays are due to lack of early stimulation in institutional settings. If a child is not spoken and read to or interacted with on a regular basis, language will not thrive. Preterm infants and those who are prenatally exposed to alcohol are also more likely to be language delayed.

Many people think of speech as a collection of words; however, much more is involved in communication. Some children experience problems with speech mechanics, including difficulties with articulation – the correct use of the tongue, lips, and jaw to produce the right sounds. In addition, those children prenatally exposed to alcohol can have a high arched palate, which causes difficulty with clarity of speech.

Children who experience early deprivation also can have problems with *expressive* language; they may use the wrong names to identify objects, change the order of words in a sentence, or have decreased vocabularies. Some children may have trouble *processing* language; although their hearing is fine, they are unable to make sense of certain words or sentences. Other children may have difficulties with the pragmatic use of language: they are unable to use language in a socially meaningful way.

Developmental and linguistic problems may emerge when a child is faced with an abrupt change of language. If a child is verbal, it is not unusual for him to relinquish his original language. Some children need help adjusting to new sounds, especially if their previous learning environment was insufficient. Unfortunately, many internationally adopted children are delayed in their native language, which further hinders their ability to acquire a new language.

Hearing loss, either temporary or permanent, also interferes with a child's developing ability to speak and to comprehend language. Preterm infants, children exposed to alcohol in-utero, and children with multiple ear infections are more likely to experience conductive hearing loss and delayed acquisition of speech. Before communication issues can be addressed, families should have the child's hearing tested.

Mild developmental language delays caused by poor orphanage conditions often diminish once the child is in a more stimulating and nurturing environment. For children whose delays are more severe, speech therapy can result in great gains, and with early intervention, the great majority of language-delayed children can make dramatic progress in their long-term language development. We recommend that if your child is over 18 months at the age of adoption, you seek out a speech and language evaluation within three months of bringing your child home. For younger children, consult your pediatrician to help determine if further assessment is warranted.

## Motor development

Many published studies have found that gross and fine motor delays are the most prevalent of the developmental lags in internationally adopted young children. These delays are usually present at the time of adoption and often continue after the children come to their new home. Restricted space for movement, lack of opportunity for exploratory play, and limited outside recreational activity all contribute to gross motor delays. Additionally, lack of experience with age-appropriate toys, decreased tummy time playing on the floor, and minimal fine motor play can lead to visual-motor coordination delays.

Accelerated or "catch-up" development is common once the children come to their new homes. Although some children require physical therapy to address gross motor delays, when provided with opportunities to participate in typical childhood activities – jumping, climbing, running, bike riding – most children will reach age appropriate gross motor developmental levels. If a child continues to have problems in gross motor development, her vision should be checked to make sure that vision problems are not contributing to a visual-motor coordination disorder. Children with fine motor delays will benefit from exposure to activities that increase eye-hand coordination, but may require occupational therapy to bolster fine motor development. Visual-motor coordination difficulties may be reflective of learning disabilities and if they persist beyond the preschool period, a learning evaluation may be warranted.

## Adaptive behavior

Internationally adopted children face the task of transforming their orphanage survival skills into functional family and school relationships. The children have to learn new patterns of behavior and new ways of interacting socially with both adults and peers. Remember that the children are being totally uprooted from an environment in which they have learned how to function and have been transplanted into one that is totally strange and in many ways bizarre. They need to learn how to function in this new environment, one in which the rules are totally different. Appropriate behavior needs to be learned in context of this new environment. In internationally adopted post-institutionalized children, adjustment to a new life often revolves around the issue of self-regulation of behavior and emotions. The children's early experiences often included rigid routines combined with a lack of control over their environment. Multiple changing caregivers can add to the significant sense of instability and helplessness.

It already has been noted that language delays are very common in internationally adopted children. Language forms the basis for other cognitive functions besides speech, such as memory, abstract reasoning and goal-oriented behavior. Children who have not experienced verbal communication do not develop an understanding of cause and effect behavior and may seem like they are tuning adults out, are defiant, or have attention deficit disorder. Lack of early stimulation impedes a child's capacity to learn the meaning of non-verbal communication as well, which translates into poor or inappropriate social skills later on. A child who did not have the benefit of a caretaker who frequently mirrored the infant's own expressions or was not shown the natural expressions of the caretaker over the course of infancy may not be able to read the facial expressions and body gestures of others. This may lead to inappropriate interpersonal responses and social skills. Many of the children have difficulty understanding and reading nonverbal cues as well. Hostility, aggression, distractibility, hyperactivity and poor attention span often have their roots in the child's frustration, uncertainty, and the inability to communicate. When identified early, it is possible to intervene to help the children development appropriate language skills, which will improve behavior.

## Sensory Integration

The concept of Sensory Integration (SI) was first introduced by Jean Ayres, an Occupational Therapist. Sensory integration is the process by which the brain receives, organizes and interprets information from the environment. The information is received by sensory receptors, such as the eyes, nose, ears, fingers, mouth and skin. Sensations such as movement, body awareness, touch, sight, sound and the pull of gravity make up the overall sensory experience. The information that is received from the environment is then sent to the corresponding regions of the brain where it is interpreted and organized. This process is what gives us our perception of the world. In children, it provides a crucial foundation for later, more complex learning and behavior. Proper sensory integration helps us to maintain attention and build positive relationships with others. All of these things contribute to positive self esteem as well as the ability to learn and concentrate. In children, it provides a crucial foundation for later, more complex learning and behavior.

For most children, sensory integration develops in the course of ordinary childhood activities. When the process of sensory integration acquisition is disrupted, due to factors such as a lack of stimulation or movement over a long period of time, sensory processing difficulties can arise. Lack of stimulation in the early years of development, such as a limited variety of foods and textures in the diet or limited opportunity for movement, play and exploration, contributes to sensory integration problems. Sensory integration dysfunction can result when babies are unable to explore their surroundings, are left alone in their cribs for long periods of time, and do not receive the nurturing touch of a caretaker. Likewise, these problems can occur in children who have been hospitalized early or for long periods of time, or in those who have suffered from some sort of trauma and disruption in their developmental process. Moreover, the neurological impact of prenatal exposure to alcohol also disrupts normal sensory processing.

Children who are experiencing sensory integration difficulties are not intentionally misbehaving. They are simply trying to gain the input that their body needs or avoid the extra stimulation in order to function properly. Children with sensory processing problems often feel uncomfortable in their own skin, agitated or out of sorts. These children are often intelligent and struggle to control their body and their need for these sensory inputs. It is important to remember that the sensory needs of these children are just that – needs. Trying to diminish the needs for these behaviors will not be effective, but finding adaptable ways to satisfy the sensory needs of the child is the effective way to help a child who is experiencing sensory processing dysfunction.

Some signs that your child may be experiencing difficulty with sensory integration include:

- Clumsy behaviors
- Over sensitivity to sounds, sights, smell, touch or movement
- Under reactivity to sounds, sights, smell, touch or movement
- Distractibility
- Hard to calm down
- Difficulty during transitions and adapting to changes in routine
- Picky when eating – particularly sensitive to the texture or feel of foods
- Resistant to touching things – e.g., resists going barefoot in the grass, playing in sand
- Defensive to light touch
- Agitation when spinning or roughhousing
- Excessive seeking out of spinning or swinging movements
- Tendency to exhibit rocking or swaying body movements
- Increased excitation during play to the point that he cannot calm down
- Distractibility when eating in a noisy environment
- Easily tired
- Weakness in various muscles
- Fear or intolerance of sounds – e.g., holds hands over ears to protect himself from sounds
- Awareness of noises that others do not notice
- Difficulties with teeth brushing, hair washing and/or bathing
- Sensitivities to clothing textures and/or needs tags cut out of clothing
- Overly fearful or avoidant of situations or people
- Impulsivity or exhibiting "daredevil" behaviors
- Difficulty falling or staying asleep.

An Occupational Therapist, trained in sensory integration assessment and treatment, can evaluate your child and provide the services that will help address these problems.

## References

New Kids, New Challenges International Adoption Clinic at the University of Minnesota. www.filenet.software.umn.edu:8471/eds/iac/home.html. Downloaded on 1-16-06.

Albers, L.H., Johnson, D.E., Hostetter, M.K., Iverson, S.I., Georgieff M.K., Miller, L.C.(1997) Health of children adopted from the former Societ Union and Eastern Europe: Comparison with pre-adoptive medical records. Journal of the American Medical Association, 278.

Hough, S. (1999). Risk factors for speech and language development of children adopted from Eastern Europe. In T. Tepper, L. Hannon, & D. Sandstrom (Eds.), International adoption: Challenges and opportunities (pp. 108-128). Meadowlands, PA: First Edition.

Johnson, D.E., Miller L.C., Iverson S.I., Franchino W., Dole K., Kiernan M.T., Georgieff M.K., and Hostetter M.K (1993). Post-placement catch-up growth in Romanian orphans with psychosocial short stature. Pediatric Research, 33.

Miller, L.C. and Hendrie, N.W. (2000) Health of Children Adopted From China Pediatrics,105.

Miller, L.C., Kiernana, M.T., Mathers M.I., and Klein-Gitelman, M. (1995). Developmental and Nutritional Status of Internationally Adopted Children. Pediatrics and Adolescent Medicine, 149 (1).

*Risk and Promise*

# Chapter 8
# Problems with
# attachment and
# emotional development[1]

Children adopted from orphanages or neglectful foster care settings often spend long hours in isolation, hours in which no one speaks to, holds, or plays with the child. The only time a child is held may be when he is being bathed or clothed. Because orphanages employ a staff of rotating workers, no one person is responsible for the primary care of any particular child. Therefore, babies from orphanages lack the opportunity to become attached to a primary caregiver. This missed opportunity can affect a child's capacity to develop emotionally connected interpersonal relationships in the future.

Child development research clearly shows that deprivation of affection, stimulation, and responsive caretaking from one or two specific caregivers can damage a child's physical, cognitive, and emotional development. Children who are neglected in their first two years of life may develop a set of peculiar behaviors, a condition called "institutional autism." These children display behaviors such as being withdrawn, sullen, and resistant to touch and have repetitive, self-stimulating behaviors such as head banging and rocking. The children also often exhibit indiscriminate friendliness and affection, something that can make adoptive parents feel good at first until they realize that the child may treat strangers more affectionately than family members.

The psychological effects of trauma and the lack of a consistent attachment relationship can cause post-institutionalized children to develop additional behavioral problems, especially in the realm of relationships with others. Even though the children are in good adoptive homes, they may be unable to

[1] *Dafna Lender, LCSW, contributed to this chapter.*

utilize their stable and caring environment to develop a sense of security and to rely on their parents in an age-appropriate way. These behaviors may manifest as indifference to others, and children may insist on doing things independently, not even thinking of asking for help when the task is clearly beyond their capacity. When distressed, they may not seek comfort from their parent, and may even seek out a stranger for comfort in the presence of their parent. Indeed, these children often are indiscriminately friendly, showing no initial cautiousness with unfamiliar people. Moreover, they may seem to prefer strangers. They also may exhibit sneaky behaviors and aggressiveness towards peers or animals.

An adjustment period and transient behavioral issues are to be expected from children coming from an early life of deprivation. The intensity, frequency and duration of any symptoms are critical to determining if professional help is warranted. It is important to seek out professional help if problems such as sleep difficulties, unusual eating behaviors, aggression, anxiety, depression, sexual acting out, or impaired school functioning persist.

## Reactive Attachment Disorder

Attachment is a process of development that typically occurs during the first three years of life. Children who, by virtue of their orphanage experience, have missed out on this crucial developmental period will likely show some degree of attachment problems. The more extreme form, Reactive Attachment Disorder (RAD), occurs in both domestic and overseas adoptions, particularly those involving older children. It is advised that you seek professional interventions if your child does not seem to be forming attachments in a reasonable period of time (approximately six months). The behavioral patterns of Reactive Attachment Disorder may include:

- lack of eye contact,
- lack of acceptance of nurturance or affection
- indiscriminant comfort seeking
- manipulative: superficially engaging
- inappropriately demanding and clingy
- hypervigilance
- stealing

- hoarding or gorging of food
- lack of a conscience
- cruelty to animals and other children,
- fire setting

## *Post-traumatic Stress Disorder (PTSD)*

Children who have been adopted from overseas can demonstrate symptoms of complex posttraumatic stress disorder years after the adoption. PTSD is a delayed expression of severe trauma that can continue to haunt the child throughout his life. Behaviors may include:

- Anxiety
- Poor emotional affect and control of impulses
- Alterations in consciousness (seeming to "space out," sensation of leaving their body)
- Damaged self-perception (sense of being different, ineffective)
- Disrupted interpersonal relationships (either mistrusting or having an extreme dependency on adults)
- Feelings of hopelessness
- Somatization (feeling chronic physical pain not explained by medical causes)
- Self regulatory difficulties: sleeping, eating, and nightmares.

# Chapter 9
# Attention Deficit
# Hyperactivity Disorder

When prospective parents think about long term behavior problems for their child, they often think of Attention Deficit Hyperactivity Disorder (ADHD). ADHD is by far the most common behavior difficulty diagnosed in the children after adoption from overseas. We will discuss classic ADHD, but it is important for parents to remember that while many of the behavioral difficulties they see in their children can look like ADHD, they may actually be symptoms of emotional difficulties. Evaluation by a professional knowledgeable about issues of internationally adopted children can help sort out the source of the behaviors.

ADHD is characterized by inattention, hyperactivity, and impulsivity. While ADHD in school-aged children has been studied extensively, little research has addressed the disorder in preschoolers, the age range in which many children are adopted from overseas. It is difficult to differentiate ADHD from normal preschool behavior because the characteristic symptoms of ADHD – inattention, impulsivity, and hyperactivity – can be normal in this age range. In children without ADHD, these behaviors are temporary and most of them "grow out of it". Far less than half of the children who show these behaviors in their early years will continue to have them in later childhood or adolescence. You cannot reliably tell the difference between those young children who will develop persistent ADHD and the majority of children who have developmentally appropriate and transient behaviors that will not be a problem long term. Clues that may help predict whether the behaviors are likely to persist are the severity of the symptoms, their pervasiveness across different settings, and their duration.

Diagnostically, the difficulties we see in many young children who have been adopted from overseas are best classified as Regulatory Disorders, as described in *Diagnostic Classification of Mental Health and Developmental Disorders of Infancy and Early Childhood.* This specific classification system for young children was developed because conventional adult psychiatric diagnoses do not adequately describe and explain the clinical presentation of many young children. This is an important concept for parents adopting from overseas.

The behavioral and sensory characteristics seen in some internationally adopted children with Regulatory Disorders include problems in all aspects of behavioral and physiological regulation:

- motor disorganization
- constant motion
- impulsivity
- an inability to settle down
- poorly differentiated fine motor activity
- over-reactivity to the sensation of movement
- difficulty using visual-spatial cues
- auditory processing problems
- language processing problems
- difficulty modulating emotional expression (moving rapidly from being calm to being out of control)
- difficulty interacting with others (either due to avoidant or overly attached behaviors)
- difficulty adapting to change
- aggression
- sleep disturbance.

While this seems to be a lengthy list of problematic behaviors, they are all associated with the children's difficulty processing the information and sensations that they receive from internal and external sources.

The observable behaviors of a specific type of Regulatory Disorder, the *Motorically Disorganized, Impulsive* pattern, can look quite similar to the classic picture of ADHD. Children in this diagnostic classification have a high activity level that is disorganized, impulsive and often purposeless. In general, the children have difficulty organizing themselves into a calm and positive state, particularly in the face of tension. This tension can be created by sensory stimulation or stress. When the children are in a situation in which they feel tension or stress, they seek ways to reduce the negative feeling by discharging the stress through behaviors that can be disruptive. While the discharge behavior may not appear to be adaptive because it often creates more problems for the child, it does serve the child's immediate need to get relief from the intolerable feeling of stress or tension. Parents often articulate this very well when they say that it feels as if their children need to get into a fight so they can cry and release tension.

Children with sensory processing difficulties also can present as being *under-reactive* to sensory stimulation. In this case, the children seek contact and stimulation through significant physical pressure, such as head banging or intruding into other people's physical space. This can manifest as the child's hitting without being provoked. The children do not respond to, and therefore cannot pay attention to, usual levels of sensory information such as voices that are not raised. This leads the children to seek out high levels of sensory input (lights turning on and off, the sensation of hitting their head, tearing up material) to satisfy their need for stimulation. While these behaviors overlap with classic patterns of ADHD, such as distractibility, difficulty sustaining attention, impulsivity, and problems following instructions, the unanswered question is whether the young child with a Regulatory Disorder will necessarily become the school-aged child with ADHD.

For younger children, the decision to prescribe medication for ADHD-type symptoms is quite difficult. Because preschoolers lack the reasoning skills, social development, and academic skills of school-aged children, interventions that are successful with older children may be ineffective in younger children. It is important to try behavioral treatment strategies tailored for the preschooler before your physician moves on to prescribing medication. However, there are some very young children who can benefit from treatment with medication for ADHD symptoms. Failing to treat them can compromise their safety, place them at increased risk for school failure, and may result in a worsening of their behavioral problems when they reach the academic challenges of elementary school.

While recent studies of treatment of young children with ADHD have concluded that medication can improve compliance, on-task behavior, and activity levels of young children with inattention, impulsivity, and hyperactivity, reviews of the studies have noted limitations of the results. Without clear guidance from research, the decision of whether to prescribe medication for a young child must be made by the physician and the parents with the focus of enhancing the child's social, academic, and family life. Above all else, however, behavioral interventions should be implemented before consideration of medications to manage behavior.

# Chapter 10
# Easing the transition
# from orphanage to home

Preparing for your child's transition from the orphanage to your home is critical to the adjustment period for parents, children, and siblings. On your visits to the orphanage, it is useful to determine if there is a caregiver who is particularly attached to your child, who is aware of his schedule and can tell you about the child's responses to various situations. Most importantly, try to find the caretaker at the orphanage who appears most affected by the child leaving the orphanage. This person can provide important information about the child and should be consulted to gain information about your child's personality, likes and dislikes, developmental skills, habits, play, etc. Moreover, having had this relationship also bodes well for the child's long term development, because there is a greater likelihood that he has experienced something resembling a primary attachment relationship with this caretaker. Having a picture of this person who has been a part of your child's life is important, and she can help in selecting a transitional object from the orphanage that can be brought home to help ease your child's adjustment.

Once you bring your child home, consistency and predictability are essential; routines allow children to feel more secure and help decrease anxiety. Young children will realize that everything has changed, but will not be able to understand the meaning or permanency of these changes. A primary goal of this transition is to help your child begin to understand that you are her primary caretaker, and that you will meet all her physical and emotional needs. It will be important to begin the attachment process by spending a great deal of time with your child. Avoid sending your child to day care or a prolonged school day if you can help it, and limit visits with relatives and friends. The first six months to a year should be reserved for you, the child's primary caretaker, to nurture and care for the child almost exclusively if possible, as would be done for a newborn. If at all possible during this initial period, one of the adoptive parents should be available to the child at all times. As you live with your child, physical touch and playfulness should be gradually introduced into the child's daily routine. Making eye contact, smiling, hugging, rocking, feeding your child and singing to her are all excellent teaching tools for developing the child's capacity to give and receive affection and receive nurturance.

Most likely there will be some developmental regression (e.g., toileting accidents) during the adjustment period. It is not unusual for children from orphanages to be accustomed to group sleeping arrangements, and to have difficulty transitioning to sleeping independently. Nightmares, night terrors, and bedwetting in older children are commonly experienced in the first few months after adoption. Creating consistent and nurturing bedtime routines and rituals can aid in the process of establishing good sleep habits.

Children may have difficulty trying different foods, especially if their new diet is substantially changed from what they ate in their birth country. Many children hoard food, overstuff their mouths, or are averse to trying new textures. Offering a variety of foods to help expand the child's eating repertoire, while not engaging in power struggles at mealtimes, can serve to facilitate a more adaptive diet.

Many children who have been living in orphanages have not experienced nurturing touch. It may take time for the child to feel comfortable and trusting while being held, hugged, rocked or touched in any way. Depending on the age of your child, gradual steps to promote physical contact may include sitting on your lap, holding your hand, offering brief hugs, or placing your hand on his shoulder. It can be helpful to be involved in an activity so that touching your child feels less intrusive to him. For example, invite him to sit on your lap while playing a game, or sit next to each other while reading a story.

Keep in mind that your child likely missed many important experiences that are typically part of infant and early childhood development. Playing "baby games" such as *Hide and Go Seek,*

*This Little Piggy, Counting Toes* and *Peek-a-Boo* are very helpful in bringing the child backwards in time psychologically, so that she can receive some of the fun and delightful attention that infants love and need. For a baby, the use of a "snuggly" to carry her allows closeness and can help with tactile stimulation as well. Holding the small child while feeding and looking at the child also promotes positive attachment. If a toddler is used to feeding herself, you can sit with her during feeding times and make mealtime enjoyable by playing interactive games (e.g., *"Here comes the airplane into the hanger..."*), singing or playing music.

The process of learning that you are the one who will provide comfort in times of physical and emotional upset involves the accumulation of daily experiences that build trust. Make a "big deal" of caring for hurts of any severity, including invisible hurts, old as well as new, by providing attention, a band-aid, or a kiss. Any activities in which your child interacts with you and takes pleasure in your company increases the strength of the parent-child bond. Children at first may be uncomfortable with direct parent-initiated eye contact, so it is important to respond sensitively to their initiation of eye contact and not pursue this to the point of intrusiveness.

Another way to deepen the connection between you and your child is to provide opportunities for your child to imitate you. This can be accomplished by offering the same activities for your child to do side by side with you. For example, if you are cooking in the kitchen, invite your child to help, or give him bowls and spoons so he can pretend to do the same thing as you are doing. If you are raking leaves, provide him with a child-sized rake and encourage him to copy you.

It is important that the post-institutionalized child learn the language of emotions. Because of the emotional deprivation they endured, some adopted children need extra help in recognizing and responding to their own and other's emotional cues. One way to help is to be an "affectively attuned" parent. This means being particularly sensitive to the child's facial expressions, such as sadness, fear, excitement, or joy, and remarking upon that feeling aloud to the child. Frequent statements such as "Boy, it looks like you really liked that toy you saw!" or, "It looks like that noise really startled you!" should be a regular part of your conversation with the child.

Making these observations in an emotional and slightly exaggerated tone will help the child begin to make connections between her feelings and her actions, which will lead to her ability to share her feelings and ask for help. Finally, try to increase opportunities to share positive emotions, such as surprises, laughing, gentle humor and teasing.

When dealing with your child's negative feelings such as anger, accept these thoughts and feelings without showing anger yourself, but provide natural and logical consequences for misbehaviors. If you are angry and feel that it is necessary to express anger to your child, express it briefly, rather than showing prolonged anger or annoyance. When you need to reprimand or provide a consequence for the child's misbehavior, try to quickly "reconnect" once the episode is over by initiating playful interaction or closeness. This will help to reduce the shame that post-institutionalized children often feel when they are told "no" or are given limits.

In addition to being emotionally attuned, accepting of feelings and being playful with your post-institutionalized child, it is crucial that you, the adult, be in charge. Children who have lived in an orphanage are used to a highly structured and rigid routine; therefore, their home life initially should have structured daily routines. Make choices that you know are in your child's best interest and structure activities so that expectations are clear. Furthermore, limit choice of activities, as your child likely will become overwhelmed by a wide variety of options. A trip to the grocery store may be more than your child can handle initially, not to mention a museum or amusement park. It is your job to assess what your child can handle and avoid situations that you know will lead to your child feeling over stimulated and out of control.

To build a strong identity, children need their own "story" of their lives told to them over and over again until they can repeat it themselves. Wonder aloud about what things were like for the child while she was in the orphanage; reminisce with her about what it was like when you first met each other. It is natural and healthy for adopted children to be curious and wonder about their birth family. Give your child permission to wonder aloud with you about her birth family's whereabouts and history, so that she will understand that it is okay to discuss these thoughts and feelings with you.

It is very useful for adoptive parents to know a few words in the child's native language and to encourage a cultural connection to his home country. This gives the child the message that the past is a valued part of his identity. However, follow the child's lead as to how much he would like to immerse himself in his native culture; some children are not interested and come to resent their adoptive parents' attempts to incorporate their native cultural elements. In these cases it may be better to back off. You can get advice on handling such situations from a professional with expertise in working with internationally adopted children.

Of course the tricky part comes when parents have to face the challenges inherent in building trust while at the same time establishing behavioral expectations and ground rules for their child. This is where a professional working with you and your family can help you to decide what is important in providing discipline and guidance to your child and where the boundaries should be set. Professional input is especially helpful when the parents cannot tell what is normal infant and child behavior as opposed to behaviors warranting intervention.

# Part III  Work Sheets for observing your child overseas and back at home

## Growth charts

The growth charts on the following pages were published by the Centers for Disease Control and Prevention, United States Department of Health and Human Services. The information is based on the normal growth curves of children in the United States. Unfortunately, there are no large published data sets for expected growth for children overseas, especially for those who come from institutionalized or foster care settings. The best thing to do is to use these growth charts keeping this caveat in mind.

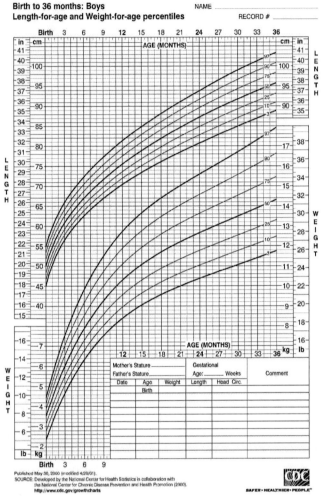

**Birth to 36 months: Boys**
**Length-for-age and Weight-for-age percentiles**

NAME _____

RECORD # _____

Published May 30, 2000 (modified 4/20/01).
SOURCE: Developed by the National Center for Health Statistics in collaboration with
the National Center for Chronic Disease Prevention and Health Promotion (2000).
http://www.cdc.gov/growthcharts

SAFER · HEALTHIER · PEOPLE™

**Birth to 36 months: Girls**
**Length-for-age and Weight-for-age percentiles**

NAME _____

RECORD # _____

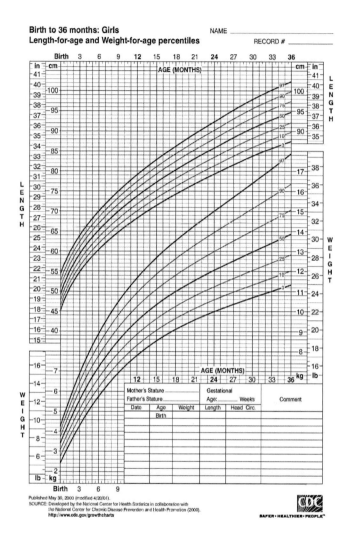

Published May 30, 2000 (modified 4/20/01).
SOURCE: Developed by the National Center for Health Statistics in collaboration with
the National Center for Chronic Disease Prevention and Health Promotion (2000).
http://www.cdc.gov/growthcharts

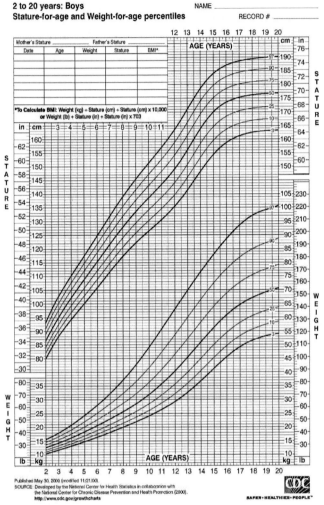

**2 to 20 years: Boys**
**Stature-for-age and Weight-for-age percentiles**

NAME _____

RECORD # _____

Published May 30, 2000 (modified 11/21/00).
SOURCE: Developed by the National Center for Health Statistics in collaboration with
the National Center for Chronic Disease Prevention and Health Promotion (2000).
http://www.cdc.gov/growthcharts

SAFER • HEALTHIER • PEOPLE™

**2 to 20 years: Girls**
**Stature-for-age and Weight-for-age percentiles**

NAME

RECORD #

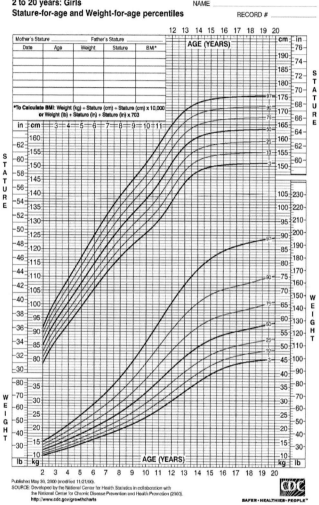

Published May 30, 2000 (modified 11/21/00).
SOURCE: Developed by the National Center for Health Statistics in collaboration with
the National Center for Chronic Disease Prevention and Health Promotion (2000).
http://www.cdc.gov/growthcharts

**CDC**

SAFER · HEALTHIER · PEOPLE™

### Birth to 36 months: Boys
### Head circumference-for-age and
### Weight-for-length percentiles

NAME _____

RECORD # _____

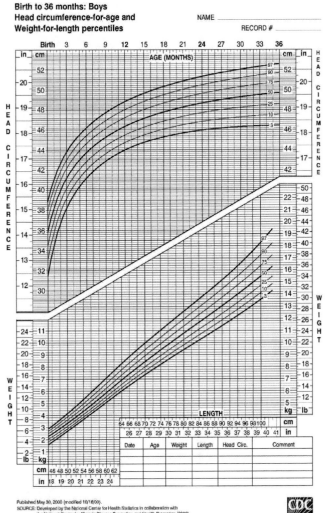

Published May 30, 2000 (modified 10/16/00).
SOURCE: Developed by the National Center for Health Statistics in collaboration with
the National Center for Chronic Disease Prevention and Health Promotion (2000).
http://www.cdc.gov/growthcharts

SAFER · HEALTHIER · PEOPLE™

## Birth to 36 months: Girls
### Head circumference-for-age and
### Weight-for-length percentiles

NAME _____

RECORD # _____

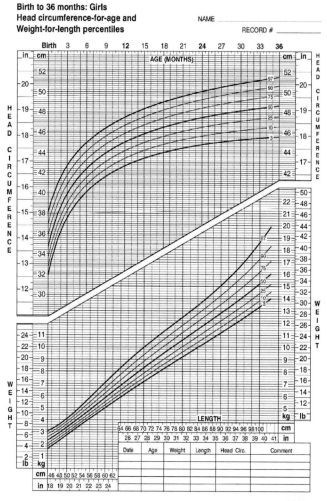

Published May 30, 2000 (modified 10/16/00).
SOURCE: Developed by the National Center for Health Statistics in collaboration with
the National Center for Chronic Disease Prevention and Health Promotion (2000).
http://www.cdc.gov/growthcharts

## *Head Circumference (cm)\* for older children*
### Girls

| Age | 3rd percentile | 50th percentile | 97th percentile |
|---|---|---|---|
| 4 years | 48.4 | 50.5 | 53 |
| 5 years | 49 | 51 | 53.6 |
| 6 years | 49.8 | 52 | 54 |
| 7 years | 50.2 | 52.2 | 54.8 |
| 8 years | 50.8 | 52.9 | 55 |
| 9 years | 51 | 53 | 55.5 |
| 10 years | 51.1 | 53.8 | 56 |
| 11 years | 51.4 | 54 | 56.9 |
| 12 years | 52 | 54.6 | 57.5 |
| 13 years | 52.2 | 55 | 57.9 |
| 14 years | 53 | 55.5 | 58.1 |

### Boys

| Age | 3rd percentile | 50th percentile | 97th percentile |
|---|---|---|---|
| 4 years | 49.5 | 52 | 54.7 |
| 5 years | 50 | 52.8 | 55 |
| 6 years | 50.5 | 53.1 | 55.8 |
| 7 years | 51 | 53.8 | 56 |
| 8 years | 51.4 | 54 | 56.5 |
| 9 years | 51.8 | 54.5 | 57 |
| 10 years | 52 | 55 | 57.3 |
| 11 years | 52.2 | 55.2 | 57.8 |
| 12 years | 52.6 | 55.6 | 58 |
| 13 years | 53 | 56 | 58.5 |
| 14 years | 53.2 | 56 | 59 |

*\*To convert inches to cm, multiply the number of inches by 2.54.*

# Parent Observation Forms for On-Site Screening

## Background Information

Child's Name: _____  Date of Birth _____

Country/Region: _____

Info received from: _____

Maternal Information
Weeks of pregnancy gestation _____

Age of mother _____  Number of pregnancies _____  Number of deliveries _____

Any known use of alcohol or drugs by mother?       Yes [  ]   No [  ]

Blood tests on mother
    HIV          Pos [  ]        Neg [  ]        Unknown [  ]
    Syphilis   Pos [  ]        Neg [  ]        Unknown [  ]
    Hepatitis B Pos [  ]        Neg [  ]        Unknown [  ]
    Hepatitis C Pos [  ]        Neg [  ]        Unknown [  ]

Social and medical history of mother


Social and medical history of father


Social and medical history of siblings


Other significant family information

# Child's Medical Information

Date _____        Age (months) _____

Weight _____    Height _____    Head circumference _____
Percentile ____    Percentile ____    Percentile ____

APGAR Scores    1 minute _____    5 minutes _____

Blood tests on baby
    HIV              Pos [  ]        Neg [  ]        Unknown [  ]
    Syphilis         Pos [  ]        Neg [  ]        Unknown [  ]
    Hepatitis B      Pos [  ]        Neg [  ]        Unknown [  ]
    Hepatitis C      Pos [  ]        Neg [  ]        Unknown [  ]

## *Questions for Orphanage Staff*

In many cases, you are more likely to receive helpful information from the orphanage staff member or foster mother who is caring for your child than from administrators of the international adoption agencies. Here are some good questions to ask of the caregiver. Of course, many times this will require a translator.

Why is this child in the orphanage or in foster care?

How long has this child been in the orphanage or foster care?

What was the health of child upon entering your care?

What is the doctor's medical opinion of this child?

What significant illnesses has the child had?

What are the current effects of those illnesses?

What treatments are recommended for this child?

Today, how does this child compare with other children you have cared for?

## Developmental Status Checklist

While you are visiting with your child overseas, take this opportunity to play with him and observe his temperament and abilities. When you go back to your hotel that night, check off the observed behaviors. This list is intended to help you organize your thoughts during a very hectic time, and if you have any concerns while overseas, this checklist can help you describe your child's developmental skills to a doctor back in the U.S. or when you get home.

The developmental skills outlined here are only general guidelines based on children growing up in a supportive family environment. Children available for adoption from overseas usually have not had the developmental support they need to flourish, so be aware that most likely your child will not consistently reach milestones on time. In addition, if the child was premature, development will be more in line with gestational rather than chronological age. For this reason, when a child who was premature undergoes developmental assessment, his developmental scores will be adjusted for prematurity until two years of age.

The tasks in Section I are listed in chronological order as they should be achieved through a normal process of development. The behaviors in Section II are not chronological in development but important to note and share with your pediatrician or other consultants. The information you provide here will provide a baseline for tracking how much progress your child makes once she is with you. Of course, at any time if you have concerns about your child's development, you will need to contact a professional who can talk through these issues with you.

### Section I
Cognitive development

    ___ Responds to voice
    ___ Eyes follow moving person or object
    ___ Gazes at parents/caretaker
    ___ Smiles responsively
    ___ Turns head to locate sound
    ___ Searches for dropped object

\_\_ Bangs hands or objects playfully
\_\_ Transfers objects from hand to hand
\_\_ Inspects toy in hands
\_\_ Puts smaller objects into larger object
\_\_ Finds hidden object
\_\_ Builds tower with blocks or stacking cups
\_\_ Engages in simple game such as pat-a-cake
\_\_ Understands the concepts of big and little
\_\_ Can recall and understand experiences from recent past

## Language development

\_\_ Turns to voice
\_\_ Smiles in response to vocalization
\_\_ Vocalizes when parent/caretaker speaks
\_\_ Squeals or laughs
\_\_ Imitates speech sounds
\_\_ Vocalizes vowel sounds
\_\_ Vocalizes vowel/consonant combination (ba, da)
\_\_ Listens selectively to two words
\_\_ Responds to name
\_\_ Follows command
\_\_ Jabbers expressively
\_\_ Imitates word
\_\_ Uses gestures to indicate needs/wants (raises arms up, points)
\_\_ Uses two words appropriately
\_\_ Combines two words into sentence
\_\_ Understands "why" questions
\_\_ Uses "big" and "little"
\_\_ Maximum number of words used in a sentence
\_\_ Can repeat 3-7 numbers
\_\_ Answers "why", "what", "who", "where", and "doing" questions
\_\_ Understands actions/verbs

## Motor development

\_\_ Holds head erect (how many seconds?)
\_\_ Reaches for object
\_\_ Grasps object
\_\_ Holds object

__ Brings object to mouth
__ Plays on stomach
__ Lifts head 45 degrees
__ Pushes up form stomach supporting weight on forearms
__ Sits with support
__ Sits alone (how many seconds?)
__ Rolls from back to side
__ Rolls from front to back
__ Rolls from back to front
__ Makes effort to move forward or backward
__ Supports weight on legs
__ Pulls to standing position
__ Stands alone
__ Walks with help
__ Walks alone
__ Walks backwards
__ Holds a crayon
__ Scribbles on paper
__ Runs
__ Uses an eating utensil
__ Jumps off floor
__ Stands on one foot
__ Throws a ball
__ Takes off own clothes
__ Walk up stairs with alternation feet
__ Skips
__ Hops
__ Catches big ball
__ Bounces ball
__ Shows hand preference
__ Laces shoes
__ Copies simple geometric figures (line, cross, circle)
__ Unbuttons and buttons

### Section II
### Sensory development

__ Tolerates hugs
__ Tolerates movement play (e.g. piggyback ride)
__ Engages in rocking or head banging
__ Interested in different textures

___ Notices touch on different parts of body
___ Tolerates/enjoys various types of touch on various parts of the body
___ Comfortable with loud sounds
___ Comfortable with bright lights
___ Comfortable with movement
___ Consistently lethargic
___ Consistently agitated
___ Consistently overactive

## Emotional development

Displays the following emotions:

___ Pleasure
___ Joy
___ Sadness
___ Anger
___ Fear
___ Assertiveness
___ Frustration
___ Interest
___ Withdrawal

___ Imitates interactions with other children or caretakers

## Attachment Observations

These observations may be used to guide you in your efforts to gain information about your child's attachment-related behaviors. This information will be useful as you describe your child to a pediatrician or developmental specialist. Keep in mind that the appropriateness of many of these behaviors varies with the age of the child. For example, you would expect stranger anxiety in a child between the approximate ages of 9 and 16 months and would not expect reciprocal play in a 5-month-old. Your responses to the following questions are intended as a guide for describing behaviors related to the attachment process. When responding to the questions, please make note of any discrepancies. For instance, you might notice that the infant makes good eye contact with one of the caregivers, yet she avoids or has fleeting eye contact during your interactions.

Does your child make eye contact with you or his caregivers?

*Comments:*

When you hold your child chest-to-chest, does he prefer to look at your face rather than in another direction?

*Comments:*

When you hug your child, does she hug you back?

*Comments:*

Does your child reciprocate smiles and vocalizations?

*Comments:*

Will your child accept comfort from you or caregivers?

*Comments:*

Will your child accept guidance or direction from you or caregivers?

*Comments:*

Does your child prefer to play or interact with you, caregivers, or other children rather than being left alone?

*Comments:*

Does your child show a wide range of emotions as opposed to being emotionally flat or listless?

*Comments:*

Does your child tend to be content rather than chronically fussy?

*Comments:*

Does your child imitate your behavior when you play with him?

*Comments:*

Does your child exhibit anxiety when approached by a stranger? (Remember, you are a stranger to her.)

*Comments:*

Does your child like your help as opposed to being overly independent or self-reliant?

*Comments:*

Does your child send you clear messages about her needs?

*Comments:*

Does your child react appropriately to pain?

*Comments:*

Is your child able to engage in play that is reciprocal and rhythmic in nature?

*Comments:*

From answering these questions, if they raise any issues or you have any concerns, you should contact a professional who can discuss your answers with you and provide you some insight.

## Suggested Items to Take with You when you meet your Child

- Crayons
- Paper
- Objects that will fit inside each other (e.g., cup and block)
- Small, easily grasped brightly colored toy such as a rattle or ring
- Small stuffed animal or doll
- Small musical toy
- Lacing toy (two years and up)
- Flexible tape measure for measuring head circumference

# Recommended reading

## Activities that recapture early interactive experiences

*I love you Rituals*, by Becky Bailey. New York: Quill (HarperCollins) 2000.

*Wonderplay*, by Fretta Reitzes and Beth Teitelman from the 92nd Steet Y Parenting Center. Philadelphia: Running Press, 1995.

*Baby Games*, by Elaine Martine. Philadelphia:Running Press, 1998.

*Fun to Grow On*, by Virginia Morin. Chicago: Chicago Review Press, 1993.

*Cooperative Sports and Games Book* (I and II), by Terry Orlick. New York: Pantheon Books, Book 1 (1978) and Book 2 (1982).

# Attachment theory and techniques

*Theraplay: Helping Parent and Children Build Better Relationships Through Attachment-Based Play*, by Ann M. Jernberg and Phyllis B. Booth. San Francisco: Jossey-Bass, 1999.

*Building the Bonds of Attachment: Awakening Love in Deeply Troubled Children's Lives* (1998). New Jersey: Jason Aronson.

*Becoming Attached*, by Robert Karen. New York: Warner Books, 1994.

*Toddler Adoption: The Weaver's Craft*, by Mary Hopkins-Best. Indianapolis: Perspective Press, 1997.

*Attaching in Adoption*, by Deborah D. Gray. Indianapolis, Perspective Press, Inc., 2002.

*A Child's Journey Through Placement*, by Vera Fahlberg. Indianapolis, Ind.: Perspectives Press, 1991.

## FAS and Prenatal Drug Exposure

*The Nature of Nurture: Biology, Environment, and the Drug-Exposed Child* by Ira J. Chasnoff, MD. Chicago: NTI Publishing, 2001.

*The Listening Heart* instructional video about domestic and international adoption of children with alcohol exposure. Produced and directed by Gabe Chasnoff. Chicago: NTI Productions, 2005.

For further information or evaluation of your child, contact:

www.childstudy.org

ichasnoff@cr-triangle.org

# References

Aronson, J. E. (1999). Alcohol related disorders in international adoption. Available at http://members.aol.com/jaronmink/index.htm.

Aronson, J. E. (2002). Alcohol related birth defects and international adoption. Available at http://www.russianadoption.org/fas.htm.

Azuma SD and Chasnoff IJ. (1993). Outcome of children prenatally exposed to cocaine and other drugs: A path analysis of three-year data. Pediatrics 92:396-402.

Barkley RA, McMurray MB, Edelbrock CS, et al. (1990) Side effects of methylphenidate in children with attention deficit hyperactivity disorder: A systemic, placebo-controlled evaluatuion. Pediatrics 86:184-192.

Brown RT, Coles, CD, Smith IE, Platzman KA, Silverstein J, Erickson S, Falek A. (1991). Effects of prenatal alcohol exposure at school age: II. Attention and behavior. Neurotoxicology and Teratology 13: 369-376.

Chasnoff IJ. (2001) The Nature of Nurture: Biology, Environment, and the Drug-Exposed Child. Chicago: NTI Publishing.

Chasnoff IJ, Anson A, Hatcher R, Stenson H, Iaukea K, and Randolph L. (1998) Prenatal exposure to cocaine and other drugs: Outcome at four to six years. In: Harvey JA and Kosofsky BE (eds.) Cocaine Effects On the Developing Brain. New York, NY: Annals of the New York Academy of Science, 314-328.

Chisholm, K. (1998). A three year follow-up of attachment and indiscriminate friendliness in children adopted from Romanian orphanages. Child Development, 69 (4), 1092-1106.

Clarren SK, Alvod EC, Sumi SM, Streissguth AP, Smith DW. Brain malformations related to prenatal exposure to ethanol. (1978). J Pediatrics 92:64-67.

Coles, CD, Brown RT, Smith IE, Platzman KA, Erickson S, Falek A. (1991). Effects of prenatal alcohol exposure at school age: I. Physical and cognitive development. Neurotoxicology and Teratology 13: 357-367.

Ciompi L. (1991). Affect as central organizing and integrating factors: A new psychosocial/biological model of the psyche. British Journal of Psychiatry 159:97-105.

Connor, D. F. (2002). Preschool attention deficit hyperactivity disorder: A review of prevalence, diagnosis, neurobiology, and stimulant treatment. Journal of Developmental and Behavioral Pediatrics, 23, S1-S12.

Connor, D. F., Glatt, S. J., Lopez, I. D., Jackson, D., Melloni, R. H. Jr (2002). Psychopharmacology and aggression. I: A meta-analysis of stimulant effects on overt/covert aggression-related behaviors in ADHD. Journal of the American Academy of Child and Adolescent Psychiatry, 41, 253-261.

Cox, C., Corley, F., Turner, M., Muter, V., Adler, K., & Kalns-Timans, A. (1993). Trajectories of despair: Misdiagnosis and maltreatment of Soviet orphans. Available at http://www.adoption-research.org/despair.html.

Crenshaw, T. M., Kavale, K. A., Forness, S. R., & Reeve, R. E. (1999). Attention Deficit Hyperactivity Disorder and the efficacy of stimulant medication: A meta-analysis. In Scruggs, T. & Mastropieri, M. (Eds.), Advances in learning and behavioral disabilities, pp 135-165. Greenwich, CT: JAI Press.

Gindis, B. (2000). Detecting and remediating the cumulative cognitive deficit in school age internationally adopted post-institutionalized children. The Post, 27, 1-6.

Glaser, D. (2000). Child abuse and neglect and the brain- A review. Journal of Child Psychology & Psychiatry & Allied Disciplines, 41 (1), 97-116.

Gunnar, M. R., Bruce, J., & Grotevant, H. D. (2000). International adoption of institutionally reared children: Research and policy. Development and Psychopathology, 12, 677-693.

Howe, D. (1997). Parent reported problems in 211 adopted children: Some risk and protective factors. Journal of Child Psychology and Psychiatry and Allied Disciplines, 38 (4), 401-411.

Hughes, D. S. (1999). Adopting children with attachment problems. Child Welfare, 78 (5), 541-560.

Johnson, D. & Fein, E. (1991). The concept of attachment: Applications to adoption. Children and Youth Services Review, 13 (5-6), 397-412.

Karen, R. (1998). Becoming attached: First relationships and how they shape our capacity to love. New York: Oxford University Press.

Kazdin AE, Weisz JR. (1998). Identifying and developing empirically supported child and adolescent treatments. J Consult Clin Psychol. 66:19-36.

Koeske, G., & Koeske, R. (1990). The buffering effect of social support on parental stress. American Journal of Orthopsychiatry, 60, 440-451.

Koot, H. M., Van Den Oord, E. J. C. G., Verhulst, F. C., & Boomsma, D. I. (1997). Behavioral and emotional problems in young preschoolers: Cross cultural validity of the Child Behavior Checklist/2-3. Journal of Abnormal Child Psychology. 25 (3), 183-196.

Kranowitz, CS. (1998). The Out-of-Sync Child. New York: Skylight Press.

McCarty, C., Waterman, J., Burge, D., &, Edelstein, S. B. (1999). Experiences, concerns, and service needs of families adopting children with prenatal substance exposure: Summary and recommendations. Child Welfare, 78 (5), 561-577.

McGinn, M. F. (2000). Attachment and separation: Obstacles for adoptees. Journal of Social Distress and Homelessness, 9 (4), 273-290.

McGoey, K. E. (2002). Early intervention for preschool-age children with ADHD: A literature review. Journal of Emotional and Behavioral Disorders, need page numbers.

Mainemer, H., Gilman, L. C., & Ames, E. W. (1998). Parenting stress in families adopting children from Romanian orphanages. Journal of Family Issues, 19 (2), 164-180.

Masten, A. S., Best, K. M., & Garmezy, N. (1991). Resilience and development: Contributions from the study of children who overcome adversity. Development and Psychopathology, 2, 425-444.

Mattson S, Riley EP, Sowell ER, Jernigan TL, Sobel DF, Jones KL. (1996). A decrease in the size of the basal ganglia in children with fetal alcohol syndrome. Alcoholism: Clinical and Experimental Research 20:1088-1093.

O'Connor, T. G., Marvin, R. S., Rutter, M., Olrick, J. T., Britner, P. A., & the English and Romanian Adoptees Study Team. (2003). Child-parent attachment following early institutional deprivation. Development and Psychopathology, 15, 19-38.

Pollack, D. & Halpern, H. (1971). An analysis of the babbling stage of institutionalized infants. Journal of Communication Disorders, 4 (4), 302-309.

Palfrey JS, Levine MD, Walker DK, et al. (1985) the emergence of attention deficits in early childhood: A prospective study. J Dev Behav Pediatr 6:339-348.

Rappley, M. D., Eneli, I. U., Mullan, P. B., Alvarez, F. J., Wang, J., Luo, Z., & Gardiner, J. C. (2002). Patterns of psychotropic drug use in very young children with attention-deficit hyperactivity disorder. Journal of Developmental and Behavioral Pediatrics, 23, 23-30.

Rutter, M. & the English and Romanian Adoptees (ERA) study team. (1998). Developmental catch-up, and deficit, following adoption after severe global early privation. Journal of Child Psychology & Psychiatry & Allied Disciplines, 39 (4), 465-476.

Siegel, D. (1999). The Developing Mind: How Relationships and the Brain Interact to Shape Who We Are, New York: Guilford Press.

Sampson P D, Streissguth A P, Bookstein F L, Little R E, Clarren S K, Dehaene P, Hanson J W, Graham J M, Jr. (1997). Incidence of Fetal Alcohol Syndrome and prevalence of alcohol-related neurodevelopmental disorder. Teratology. 56:317-326.

Sayegh, Y. & Dennis, W. (1965). The effect of supplementary experiences upon the behavioral development of infants in institutions. Child Development, 36 (1), 81-90.

Spitz, R. A. (1946). Hospitalism; a follow-up report on investigation described in Volume I, Psychoanalytic Study of the Child, 2, 113-117.

Spitz, R. A. (1949). The role of ecological factors in emotional development in infancy. Child Development, 20, 145-156.

Streissguth AP, Aase JM, Clarren SK, Randels SP, LaDue RA, Smith DF. (1991). Fetal Alcohol Syndrome in adolescents and adults. JAMA.265:1961-1967.

Riley EP, Mattson SS, Sowell ER, Jernigan TL, Sobel DF, Jones KL. (1995). Abnormalities of the corpus callosum in children prenatally exposed to alcohol. Alcoholism: Clinical and Experimental Research 19:1198-1202.

Roebuck TM, Mattson SN, and Riley EP. (1998). A review of the neuroanatomical findings in children with FAS. Clinical and Experimental Research. 22:339-344.

Shapiro MB, Rosman NP, Kemper TL. (1984). Effects of chronic exposure to alcohol on the developing brain. Neurobehavioral Toxicology and Teratology 6:351-356.

# About the Authors

**Ira J. Chasnoff, MD** is President of Children's Research Triangle and NTI Upstream. He is a Professor of Clinical Pediatrics at the University of Illinois College of Medicine in Chicago. He is one of the nation's leading researchers in the field of child development and prenatal and postnatal trauma. Dr. Chasnoff received his medical degree from the University of Texas Health Science Center at San Antonio and served a pediatric residency at Children's Memorial Hospital, Chicago. He is the author of six books and over 100 research articles on the effects of maternal drug use and child neglect on the long-term cognitive, behavioral, and learning outcomes of children. Dr. Chasnoff has published six books that explore biological and environmental factors that impact the ultimate development of young children and present practical strategies for helping children reach their full potential at home and in the classroom. The recipient of several national and international awards for his work with high risk women, children, and families, Dr. Chasnoff for several years has been selected by a poll of physicians across the nation for listing in America's Best Doctors.

**Linda D. Schwartz, PhD** is a Licensed Clinical Psychologist with a specialization in Child and Family Psychology. She is the Clinical Director at the Child Study Center in Chicago, where clinicians provide medical, developmental and psychological evaluations, as well as therapy, for at risk children, most of whom are adopted or in the foster care system. Dr. Schwartz has nineteen years of clinical and research experience with children and adolescents who have a variety of developmental, behavioral and emotional disorders.

**Cheryl L. Pratt, PhD** is a Pediatric Clinical Nurse Specialist, Developmental Psychologist, and an Infant Mental Health Specialist. Her work focuses on children at risk from early abandonment and trauma with a specialization in attachment and maternal/infant interaction. Dr. Pratt has taught at St. Xavier University, Loyola University of Chicago, Governors State University, and the Erikson Institute for Advanced Child

Development and has presented nationally on a range of Infant Mental Health issues as well as developmental and social-emotional screening and assessment in young infants. Her research interests include the study of parent-child relationships in dyads experiencing perinatal vulnerability, substance abuse, and other pediatric chronic and acute illnesses. Currently Dr. Pratt works at the Child Study Center in Chicago, Illinois as the Coordinator for the infant/toddler team and oversees clinical training programs.

**Gwendolyn J. Neuberger, MD** is a board-certified pediatrician at Children's Research Triangle, specializing in preadoption assessments for international adoption. Dr. Neuberger received her medical degree and served a pediatric residency at Emory University School of Medicine in Atlanta, Georgia.